"These materials are Bibl[...] liever in an interactive, p[...] process of God's purposes for fruitful and victorious living."

Dr. John Orme, Executive Director,
Interdenominational Foreign
Mission Association

"Some of the best discipleship materials I have seen. I appreciate the centrality of Scripture and the Christ-centered focus."

Dr. Hans Finzel, Executive Director,
CBInternational

"The power of these books comes from the lifestyle of two people who practice these truths and teach them to others."

Barry St. Clair, Founder and Director,
Reach Out Ministries

"This discipleship curriculum is easy to read and easy to use. I heartily recommend it for [those] who desire to know Christ and make Him known."

Dr. George Murray, President,
Columbia International University,
former General Director of
The Evangelical Alliance Mission (TEAM)

Learning *to* Trust

TERRY POWELL AND BILL JONES

CHRISTIAN PUBLICATIONS, INC.
CAMP HILL, PENNSYLVANIA

CHRISTIAN PUBLICATIONS, INC.
3825 Hartzdale Drive, Camp Hill, PA 17011
www.cpi-horizon.com
www.christianpublications.com

Faithful, biblical publishing since 1883

Learning to Trust
ISBN: 0-87509-895-9
LOC Control Number: 01-130444
© Copyright 2001 by
Crossover Communications International

01   02   03   04   05   5   4   3   2   1

For information, write:
Crossover Communications International
Box 211755
Columbia SC USA 29221

Dedication

To Carter and Libby Vann

Look up the word "hospitality"
in a dictionary, and you'll
see their pictures. What a
privilege to call them friends!
—Terry Powell

To William David Jones

May you be a man
—after God's own heart,
—one who will do all of God's will,
—one who serves the purpose of God
—in your generation.
Acts 13:22, 36
—Bill Jones

CONTENTS

Introduction

*L*earning to Trust is a Bible study guide for your individual benefit. This discipleship material will have maximum profit for you if you're a part of a group that meets on a weekly basis. A *Leader's Guide* for *Learning to Trust* is available from the publisher.

Other titles in the Daring Disciple Series include:

Knowing God
Discovering Your Identity
Walking in the Spirit
Sharing the Message

Read This First!

Fortifying Your Faith

Do you ever wish or pray for more faith? Do you ever feel frustrated because your capacity to trust God fluctuates from day to day? Do you hear stirring testimonies and yearn for the kind of faith others seem to have? If so, we can identify.

It is natural for a follower of Jesus Christ to want a closer walk with Him, to desire a sturdier faith. Rather than viewing your felt need as a sign of weakness, consider it a positive indicator of spiritual health. If a person is unaware of the need for growth, he cannot cultivate a deeper faith. But if you are yearning for a more stabilizing faith, you are a prime candidate for God's transforming work.

This book is based on the following premise: **the *product* of a stronger faith requires a *process*.** God *does not* instantly zap you with more faith. He *does* work through all sorts of circumstances and relationships with the ultimate goal of giving your faith His stamp of approval. He tests your faith, exposing the extent of your capacity to trust

Him. And in the process He strengthens it by revealing more of His trustworthiness.

Each of the chapters in this book focuses on a typical life experience that either tests the quality of your faith or threatens to destroy it. You will discover that the very circumstances that seem to hinder faith can become tools in God's hands for developing it.

"The devil is an expert advertiser. He knows how to display his wares in the most attractive setting, and he can dazzle the imagination . . . with the glamour of his commodities."[1]
—Merrill Tenney

The Test of Temptation

Temptation is _____.
A mixture of adults and teens were asked to complete that sentence. Here are a few of their responses:

- An extra piece of cake when I'm trying to lose weight.

- A voice in my head, coaxing me to stretch the truth in order to get something I want.

- When I rationalize about neglecting my quiet time because of a jam-packed schedule.

- That yearning for a new house in an upscale subdivision, when the one I have meets my needs just fine.

- When I hold a grudge against another Christian instead of confronting him for sinning against me.

- The urge to make a derogatory remark about a third party during a conversation.
- A girl in skintight jeans and braless halter top.

There is no denying that sin often comes wrapped in attractive packages. Our commitment to Christ does not dull our senses or immunize us against ungodly influences. We must realize, however, that temptation itself is not wrong. Jesus Himself was "tempted in all things as we are" (Hebrews 4:15). Only when we give in to it does temptation become sin.

Since temptation is inevitable, how can we keep it from getting the best of us? What weapons has the Lord provided to assist us in the daily grind of spiritual warfare? You can glean a partial answer to those questions by studying Matthew 4:1-11, the record of Jesus' temptation before the launch of His earthly ministry.

Read Matthew 4:1-11. These verses reveal helpful insights about our archenemy and show how Jesus passed the test posed by the devil's enticements.

Knowing Your Opponent

Are you a basketball junkie? A baseball zealot? A football fanatic? Even those who have only a passing interest in professional sports are aware that scouting the opponent is big business. A big chunk of teams' budgets goes for the salaries and travel expenses of their scouts.

If the Atlanta Braves baseball team plans to play the Los Angeles Dodgers in an important series, a scout flies to Los Angeles to watch the Dodgers against another opponent. He notes which hitters are hot or in a slump, which outfielder has the weakest arm, which pitchers are struggling with their control. Then he rushes a report back to Atlanta, full of statistics and details that could influence Atlanta's coaching strategies. Teams realize that *a knowledge of the opponent is essential to competing successfully.*

That is also true for the Christian life. Familiarity with our foe's characteristics and schemes enables us to prepare an adequate game plan. Woven through the fabric of Matthew 4:1-11 is valuable information about our spiritual nemesis and his strategies.

The Bible calls him *Satan* (which means "adversary"), or the *devil* (which means "slanderer"). He wanted Jesus to bypass the cross and follow his plan rather than God the Father's agenda. So he approached Jesus when the Lord was alone in the wilderness.

The events in Matthew 4:1-11 occurred right after Jesus' public baptism and a heavenly endorsement of Jesus' life and ministry (3:13-17). The confrontation happened immediately preceding the launch of Jesus' public ministry.

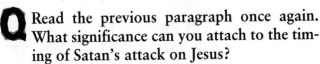 Read the previous paragraph once again. What significance can you attach to the timing of Satan's attack on Jesus?

A _____

_____

_____

Q Satan's attacks occurred *after* a spiritual "high"
(the Father's commendation) and *before* Jesus
launched His public ministry. Put your conclu-
sion about Satan's timing in the form of a principle. In what sense is timing a factor in Satan's
warfare against God's people?

A _____

_____

_____

Q What specific temptations did Satan fling at
Jesus?

A _____

_____

_____

After a forty-day fast, Satan urged Him to turn
stones to bread. Jesus' rebuttal included a quote
from Deuteronomy 8:3: "Man does not live by
bread alone, but man lives by everything that pro-
ceeds out of the mouth of the LORD." What Jesus
had in mind was not "spiritual bread," such as
God's written Word. Rather, in this instance the issue was the source of the *literal* bread needed to satisfy His hunger.

The Deuteronomy passage refers to God's provision of manna during Israel's wilderness wan-
derings. God spoke the word that created the

manna. Moses informed the Israelites that what distinguished the manna from "regular" bread was its source: *God*. The fact that manna wasn't "bread alone" meant it was unlike *regular* bread. It wasn't *just* bread. This bread was spoken into existence by God. *He* could be relied upon to sustain them and meet their needs.[2]

By quoting the verse from Deuteronomy, Jesus revealed His willingness to wait for God the Father's provision. Satan was enticing Jesus to meet a genuine physical need—hunger—outside the Father's will. To heed Satan's advice would have been equivalent to relying on an illegitimate source to meet a legitimate need. *The method of meeting a need must be approved by God.*

Satan's second lure offered Jesus a spectacular form of public recognition. "Leap from the temple pinnacle and angels will catch you," he told Jesus. Such a miraculous stunt before the crowds in the capital would have given Jesus instant recognition as the nation's Messiah. Jesus deserved the recognition. But once again, by listening to Satan, He would have gained it by means not approved by the Father. According to Craig Glickman, Jesus "would not leap from the temple and force His Father to act miraculously on His behalf. To do so would be an implicit rejection of the Father's right to determine the time and place of His miracles."[3]

Similarly, we must trust in God the Father's timing and sovereignty. Whether the desire is for a marriage companion or the recognition we feel we deserve in our profession, we cannot force

God's hand. Nor should we satisfy these desires by means apart from His will.

The third temptation reinforced and built upon the previous two. The devil offered Christ earthly kingdoms for the price of His worship. Like the bread and messianic recognition, the kingdoms were destined by God to belong to the Son. Satan offered Jesus a prize He would someday possess anyway. Again, Satan was asking Jesus to act independently of the Father, suggesting that Jesus take the easy route. However, the Father intended for the Son to die for our sins before assuming a position of honor and exaltation.

Satan tempts us to meet legitimate needs outside of the means that God has prescribed.

Q What are some legitimate physical, material and emotional needs that you have? Have you ever relied on a wrong source or an inappropriate means to satisfy one of those needs? If so, explain:

A _____
_____
_____

Q Summarize what the nature of the temptations described in Matthew 4:1-11 tells you about Satan.

A _____
_____
_____

Q The devil enticed Jesus three separate times, not just once. **What does that fact say about our foe?**

A _____

_____

_____

Satan does not give up easily. He persists in flinging temptations at us.

Q What effect should his persistence have on God's people?

A _____

_____

_____

Knowing God's Word

Q What did Jesus' reactions to the three temptations have in common?

A _____

_____

_____

Q Put Jesus' defense strategy in terms of a timeless principle. **What did He model for us about handling temptation?**

A _____

_____

_____

Review the content of the three Old Testament verses Jesus quoted: Deuteronomy 8:3, 6:16 and 6:13. **What connection do you see between the verses He selected and the temptations tossed at Him?**

A _____

_____

_____

Jesus didn't draw on just any verse in His memory. Each Scripture He quoted addressed the specific appeal or theme inherent in the temptation. Similarly, as our knowledge of the Bible increases, we can fight temptation with divine perspectives on the issue involved.

To locate Bible passages that speak to specific areas of temptation, consult a concordance or topical Bible. Ask your pastor or small group leader to show you how to match particular topics with specific Scripture sections. Here's a sampling of what we mean:

AREA OF TEMPTATION	SCRIPTURE
• Sexual fantasy or infidelity	Proverbs 5:1-23; 6:27- 35; 7:6-27 First Corinthians 6:12- 20 Philippians 4:8
• Bitterness; unforgiving spirit	Matthew 5:23-24 Hebrews 12:14-15 Ephesians 4:26-32

AREA OF TEMPTATION	SCRIPTURE
• Misuse of tongue	Proverbs 10-21 Ephesians 4:29 James 3:1-12
• Pride	Second Chronicles 26:16-23 Proverbs 16:18 First Peter 5:5-6
• Greed, materialism	Psalms 39:4-6; 49:5-12 Matthew 6:19-34 First Timothy 6:6-19
• Worry	Matthew 6:19-34 Philippians 4:6-8 First Peter 5:6-7

Q Think of a time your knowledge or memorization of a Bible passage strengthened you in the face of temptation. Briefly describe how God's Word enabled you to resist.

A _____

_____

_____

_____

You have discovered that hiding God's Word in your heart provides the perspective and the power that is needed to resist Satan. A working knowledge of the Bible provides fuel for the Holy Spirit to use daily. To consult what Scripture says about the temptation or compromising situation you're facing is a wise battle strategy. Paul encouraged the Corinthians with these words: "For though we live in the world, we do not wage war as the world does. The weapons we fight with are not the weapons of the world. On the contrary, they have divine power to demolish strongholds" (2 Corinthians 10:3-4, NIV).

Please note, however, that we are not talking about some sterile, push-button formula for reading the Bible. *God's Word helps us to resist temptation because it draws us closer to Him.* Reading it creates an intimate bond between us and its Author. Studying the Bible infuses us with God's vision for His people and for the world. We get better acquainted with the Person behind the words and our love for Him increases as our knowledge of His attributes and deeds expands. As our time in God's Word enhances our relationship with Him, the truth carries us to spiritual victory in our daily routines.

Scripture exerts a positive kind of pressure on us that keeps us within proper spiritual boundaries. Keeping this idea in mind, consider the following information.

The *Thresher* was a submarine lost in the Atlantic a few decades ago. When divers found the wreckage, they saw that some of the bulkheads had not been properly welded. When the ship sank to a certain depth, the bulkheads gave way. The men inside were cooked as if in a pressure cooker. Reports say that the sea water turned to steam as it seeped through the hull. Divers found only small pieces of the sub because the outside pressure had become so intense that without equal pressure from the inside, the *Thresher* crumpled up like a piece of paper.

Like the *Thresher*, we need pressure from within to counteract the pressure of the non-Christian environment attacking us from without. The Holy Spirit utilizes our knowledge of Scripture to generate that inward pressure. But when we neglect spiritual resources such as the Bible, prayer and fellowship with other believers, the inward pressure wanes and leaves us vulnerable to external influences.

Memorizing God's Word

A logical response to the concepts discussed in this chapter is to trust more in Jesus through a commitment to Scripture memory. The weapon Jesus used against Satan is available to you. Soak up the words of Jay Kesler on this issue:

> If you know the Bible, if you read it, and think about it, there's good material going into you. The old computer slogan, "garbage in, garbage out," really applies here. . . . Temptation demands a positive antidote. You can't waltz into a situation and then think, "I hope I don't do anything wrong." You need a positive antidote long before then. Fill up your mind with good things.[4]

You are assigned a memory verse for each chapter in this book. At the start of each group session, you will recite the verse to a partner. The verse for

Chapter 1 reminds you of Jesus' warfare strategy: Psalm 119:11.

Pick a time early in the week to digest your memory verse. Review it the same time every day until your group meets. Complete the following sentence:

The time of day I will reserve for Scripture memory is _____.

Nobody trusts God until
he has to.[1]
— Ron Dunn

The Test of Stormy Circumstances

I t is humbling to realize that deep faith in the Lord is not a natural occurrence. Usually we put our trust in Him only when we have exhausted our own resources, when everything we tried on our own fails, when we're clueless and the deadline for action is fast approaching.

Q **What are some "have to" situations adults typically face in the course of their lives?** Briefly describe a few circumstances that tend to threaten stability—that force folks to rely on God instead of themselves. One possibility to consider as a catalyst for your thinking is: Unemployment due to company downsizing.

A _____

_____

_____

_____

Which of those circumstances which threaten stability from your list have *you* encountered? What kinds of things most often pull the props out from under your sense of security? What most often leaves you feeling apprehensive or frightened?

You will be interested to know that facing threatening circumstances is nothing new for Jesus' followers. By examining Mark 4:35-41, which features Jesus' disciples as they faced a literal storm on the Sea of Galilee, you will discover insights about handling adversity that connect the distance between Palestine and your hometown and bridge the time span between the first and the twenty-first centuries. What you learn won't prevent storms, but it may sustain you when they come. You will glean principles for reacting to them in a godly manner. You will learn how threats to your security can boost your faith, instead of destroying it.

Background on Mark 4:35-41

Prior to this incident, the disciples had listened as Jesus taught in parables (Mark 4:1-34). His followers had previously witnessed several miracles: The exorcism of a demon-possessed man (1:23-28); the healing of the paralytic (2:1-12); the restoration of a man's withered hand (3:1-6); plus the turning of water into wine (John 2:1-11).

The setting for Mark 4:35-41—the Sea of Galilee—is a pear-shaped body of water approximately twelve miles long and six miles wide. Set in a basin and surrounded by hills, this inland waterway is subject to strong winds and sudden storms which are spawned by the huge Mediterranean Sea to the west. A few of Jesus' disciples had earned their living as fishermen on this same body of water (1:16-18). Although several of the disciples were experienced with boats, they were very anxious at the onset of the storm, which suggests that this particular storm was much worse than usual.

Storm Warnings

Ask the Lord to illumine your thinking as you read Mark 4:35-41. Pay close attention to details in the narrative, especially to the verbal exchanges between Jesus and the disciples. Then record your responses to the following questions:

Q What words/phrases from your Bible reveal the severity of the storm?

A _____

_____

_____

Q What words would you use to describe the disciples' reaction to the storm?

A _____

_____

_____

Q How would you describe the disciples' reaction to Jesus' miracle of calming the storm?

A _____

_____

_____

Imagine: *after* the storm was stilled they were "very much afraid" (4:41)—*of Jesus Himself.* His instantaneous stilling of the raging wind, driving rain and breaking waves left an indelible impression.

Q What did Jesus say to the disciples before they launched the trip across the water?

A _____

_____

_____

What Jesus said to the disciples prior to the storm should have affected their response to it. He said, "Let us go over to the other side" (4:35).

Q What did His words imply about their arrival on the other side of the sea?

A _____

_____

_____

In effect, Jesus promised that they would arrive safely. He didn't guarantee a trouble-free journey, but He did imply that they would climb out of the boat on the other side of the sea. If they had remembered His promise, perhaps panic would not have paralyzed them when the storm hit.

Ever since the Bible was written, God has provided perspective and sustenance to handle crises through the promises on its pages. A few of the Bible's promises have already been fulfilled. Others were time-bound, applying only to a particular person or group. Numerous promises apply to God's people of all eras because they are rooted in the character of God and His revealed will.

To whet your appetite for a lifelong feast of divine promises, consult the following verses: Isaiah 41:10; Matthew 28:20; John 14:1-3; 16:24; First Corinthians 10:13; 15:58; Philippians 4:1-9 and James 1:5.

Q What threatening circumstances came to your mind as you examined those promises?

A _____

_____

_____

Q Read the verses listed above, which contain timeless promises from God. Then write out the promise from this list that means most to you right now.

A _____

_____

_____

Jesus rebuked His followers for their lack of faith (Mark 4:40). What He said can be literally translated, "Do you *not yet* have faith?" To answer the question that follows, review the background commentary on Mark 4:35-41 (pages 18-19), as well as Jesus' words in verse 40.

Q What do the words "not yet" imply about the basis for the disciples' faith?

A _____

_____

_____

The basis for Jesus' harsh rebuke was their recent observation of His miraculous power. Despite previous exposure to Jesus' supernatural competency and His presence in the boat with them, they were scared stiff. If they had remembered Jesus' past performance and had pondered the implications of His power for their current circumstance, perhaps they would have faced the storm with more faith.

Q Describe specific ways in which you have observed the Lord's power and intervention in your past.

A _____

_____

_____

Q How should your past experience of God's faithfulness affect your response to present day trials?

A _____

_____

_____

Despite Jesus' reproof for their lack of faith (4:40), His followers did something when they were afraid that serves as a positive example for us.

Q What positive action did they model for us about responding to threatening situations?

A _____

_____

_____

Examine the following Scripture passages: Psalm 50:15; 55:22; Philippians 4:6-7; and First Peter 5:7. **In one sentence summarize the strategy for handling stability-threatening circumstances recommended by those verses.**

A _____

_____

Though He was sleeping as the disciples fought the storm's elements, Jesus was physically present with them on the boat (Mark 4:36, 38). Christians do not enjoy His physical companionship at this time but we do enjoy a privilege similar to that of the disciples.

 Look up Matthew 28:20 and John 14:16-18. **What truth can sustain you when you feel threatened?**

A _____

_____

 What attributes of Jesus does the story in Mark 4:35-41 illustrate?

A _____

_____

 When you are facing a crisis, how should your awareness of Christ's attributes affect your reaction to the situation?

By now you are aware that the narrative in
Mark 4:35-41 is full of insights for handling situations which rob you of peace. The Holy Spirit inspired the recording of such events in order to
illustrate or to suggest timeless truths. We can
identify with the predicaments faced by the Bible
characters and know that the God whom they
worshiped is the same yesterday, today and forever.

Stilling *Your* Storms

For purposes of this chapter, a "stormy situation" is any predicament that causes within you
the same emotions or reactions exhibited by Jesus' disciples: anxiety, fear and insecurity.

Q As you reflect on your current responsibilities
and relationships, is there a circumstance
looming on the horizon which may threaten
your stability? Is your faith in Christ being
tested in some painful manner? If so, describe
your "storm" in one or more sentences.

A

Now mull over the insights for handling "storms" that you gleaned from Mark 4:35-41.

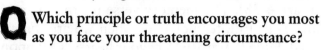

Q Which principle or truth encourages you most as you face your threatening circumstance?

A _____

_____

_____

Remember that God's ultimate goal for our lives is Christlikeness (Romans 8:29). Perhaps He allows storms because He is more interested in our character than our comfort. Changing us is a bigger priority for Him than changing our circumstances. He is aware that it may take a greater miracle to still the storm inside us than it does to remove the external threat.

Imagine that a sculptor launches a project with a huge piece of marble weighing several thousand pounds. After months of diligent, meticulous labor, he reveals the finished product—a horse. How did he do it? One way to describe the process is that he chiseled away everything in the block of marble that didn't look like a horse.

The next time you are swamped by stormy circumstances, envision God with a hammer and chisel in hand, chipping away everything in you that does not look like Jesus.

Memorizing Scripture

Perhaps the disciples' faith was weak, but what faith they had they focused on the Person of

Christ. When they felt overwhelmed by the storm they awoke Him and pleaded for His intervention (Mark 4:38). The memory verse for this chapter invites us to interrupt Him when we are threatened. Hide Psalm 50:15 in your heart: "Call upon Me in the day of trouble; I shall rescue you, and you will honor Me."

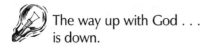 The way up with God . . . is down.

CHAPTER THREE

The Test of Hopeless Situations

Do you want to inject new vitality into your prayer life without any self-sacrifice whatsoever? Without any of the rigorous self-discipline that some people associate with spiritual consecration? Without the time that a serious devotion to prayer carves out of your schedule?

Perhaps the "Godbox" is your answer. A Christian magazine disclosed the availability of this innovative device:

> For a direct line to heaven the "Godbox" is your answer, claims A Creative Company, based in Carson City, Nevada.
>
> The Godbox is a small container made of leather-like material and gold-stamped. The Godbox is also available in wood with a lasered top. And buyers may personalize their Godboxes with their names gold-stamped on the product for an extra fee.
>
> "The box is designed to relay the owner's prayers directly to God's care," says Jerry Goossen, one of the three stockholders in the

Godbox company. "You simply write your problems or desires on a preprinted prayer sheet,
drop the prayer in the box, and let God take
over," he explains.[1]

The basic Godbox sells for $14.95, and the simu-
lated leather version is $29.95. With a lasered wood
top, a Godbox's price tag is $69.95. A few years
ago, you could actually purchase it in a few novelty
shops and religious bookstores across the country.

Of course, we *are not* recommending that you
dole out cash for a Godbox. We are astonished at
how far some people go in commercializing faith
in Christ.

If the Godbox is not the panacea for a vibrant
prayer life, what is? According to God's Word,
one surefire stimulant for a healthy prayer life is
an impossible situation. A test of faith so impos-
ing that human effort cannot pass it; a problem so
taxing that all other strategies backfire; a circumstance so helpless that the only recourse is to
throw ourselves at the Lord's feet.

That is the kind of situation faced by three people
whose stories are told in chapter 5 of Mark's Gospel. They did not need a Godbox. They wanted direct communication with Someone they thought
could alleviate their burden. By examining their en-
counters with Jesus, we find answers to the following questions:

- In what ways does the Lord test our faith?

- When a person has faith in the Lord, how
  does it show?

- What is there about Jesus that makes Him worthy of our trust?

- What should characterize us when we approach the Lord with our needs?

What you learn about trusting in the Lord in Mark 5 can save you at least $14.95.

Mark 5 Background

During the first phase of His public ministry on earth, Jesus taught and acted in ways that disclosed His identity as God's Son. Bible scholars consider Peter's confession of Jesus as the Messiah (Mark 8:29) a turning point in Jesus' ministry. Jesus performed the majority of His miracles prior to Peter's confession. The focus was on who Jesus is as distinct from a mere human being. After Peter identified Him as the Messiah, Jesus changed the emphasis of His teaching. Only then did He start referring to His impending death on the cross. The focus shifted from *who He is* to *why He came*. The three episodes in Mark 5 occurred in the earlier phase of Jesus' earthly ministry, when He sought to instill deeper faith in the disciples through their observation of His miraculous deeds.

The events in Mark 5 followed on the heels of Jesus' stilling of the storm (4:35-41). When viewed as a unit, Mark 4:35-5:43 reveals Jesus' power and authority over nature (4:35-41), Satanic forces (5:1-20); disease (5:25-34) and death (5:21-24, 35-43). Chapter 5 of Mark's Gospel adds to the list of faith-boosting principles uncovered in the previous incident on the sea.

Foe of the Faith

After Jesus exited the boat, a man tormented by numerous demons confronted Him. The demons actually took over the man's vocal cords and spoke for him. Find out what happened by reading Mark 5:1-20 slowly. Then tackle the following study questions.

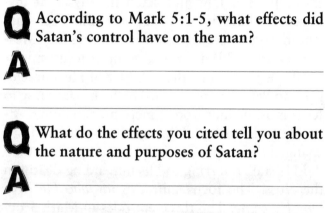

Q According to Mark 5:1-5, what effects did Satan's control have on the man?

A _____

_____

_____

Q What do the effects you cited tell you about the nature and purposes of Satan?

A _____

_____

The effects of Satan's control included extraordinary strength, social ostracism, emotional trauma and physically self-destructive habits (5:3-5). That the demon-possessed man lived "among the tombs" is interesting, because he was as dead spiritually as the inhabitants of the tombs were physically. The man's condition demonstrates Satan's destructive purpose for the lives of human beings. No matter what form satanic influence takes, the ultimate result is pain and despair. Peter called Satan an adversary who "prowls about like a roaring lion, seeking someone to devour" (1 Peter 5:8).

Q In ten words or less, describe the demons' attitude toward Jesus (Mark 5:6-13).

A _____

_____

_____

Q In what sense did the demons "believe" in Jesus?

A _____

_____

_____

Q What insight concerning faith does the demons' belief in Jesus reveal to you?

A _____

_____

_____

The demons who controlled that man acknowledged a basic truth about Jesus: *He is the Son of God*! Right belief characterized Satan throughout the New Testament. During a previous encounter Jesus had with a demoniac, a demon's voice proclaimed, "I know who You are—the Holy One of God!" (Mark 1:24). In a treatise on the necessity of works stemming from saving faith, James added, "You believe that God is one. You do well; the demons also believe, and shudder" (James 2:19).

Here is the bottom line: *Acknowledging biblical truths does not make anyone a Christian.* Entering a relationship with Christ involves a response of the will. He enters a life in response to a personal invitation which involves agreeing that we have sinned and need a Savior. It involves a change of mind about our lifestyle, a new distaste for patterns of sin and a fresh yearning to please God. Believing certain things about Jesus is essential to salvation, but it is not sufficient without a willingness to put trust in Him. The demons held correct opinions about Jesus' identity but they did not exercise *saving faith* in Him.

Q It is obvious from this instance that Jesus' power eclipsed that of Satan. **Search Mark 5:6-20 and jot down all the words/phrases that reveal the superiority of Christ in relation to Satan.**

A _____

_____

_____

Q Read First John 4:4. **How does it make you feel to know that Jesus' power far exceeds that of Satan?**

A _____

_____

_____

Q What are some situations you are currently facing in which it is important to remember Jesus' dominance of Satan?

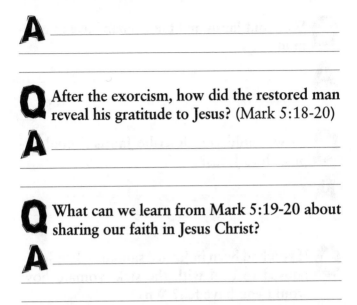

A _____

Q After the exorcism, how did the restored man reveal his gratitude to Jesus? (Mark 5:18-20)

A _____

Q What can we learn from Mark 5:19-20 about sharing our faith in Jesus Christ?

A _____

Although personal witnessing should always include biblical truths concerning God's provision for our sin, effective evangelism may also include a personal testimony during which we explain changes Jesus has made in our lives. We, too, can obey Jesus' words in Mark 5:19: "Go home to your people and report to them what great things the Lord has done for you, and how He had mercy on you."

People in Need

Now set your scope on Mark 5:21-43, which describes the plight of the synagogue official, Jairus, and an ill woman. Contemplate those verses for a few minutes, then use the following probes to dig deeper.

Q What did Jairus and the woman have in common?

A _____

_____

_____

Q How would you describe Jairus' initial approach to Jesus?

A _____

_____

_____

Q If you had been in Jairus' sandals when Jesus paused to deal with the sick woman, how would you have felt? Why?

A _____

_____

_____

Q If you were Jairus, what effect would the woman's interruption have had on your faith? Explain.

A _____

_____

_____

Q What facts revealed the desperation of the woman who interrupted Jesus?

A _____

_____

Q How did both Jairus and the woman demonstrate trust in Jesus for their need?

A _____

_____

_____

Q Pay close attention to the physical posture of Jairus (Mark 5:22), and the woman (see the parallel version of this story in Luke 8:47). **What did their posture suggest about their attitude in relation to Jesus?**

A _____

_____

_____

Three in One

Q Now reflect on all three episodes in Mark 5 as a unit. **What specific, timeless truths about faith do the episodes offer?** To serve as a catalyst for your thinking and to provide categories for your consideration of this question, mull over the implications of:

a. *the attributes of Jesus demonstrated in Mark 5.*
b. *the way the characters approached Jesus.*
c. *the ways in which these characters' faith was tested or challenged.*
d. *the stark contrast in the characters* before *and* after *their encounter with Jesus.*

A _____

_____

_____

_____

_____

An Apt Approach

One thread of thought weaving together the episodes in Mark 4:35-5:43 is the characters' approach to Jesus. Those individuals did what Jesus encourages all His followers to do: "Come to Me, all who are weary and heavy-laden, and I will give you rest" (Matthew 11:28).

The comments that follow trace this theme through the four incidents in Mark 4:35-5:43. The remarks also capture several of the truths you have identified through the Bible study questions in this chapter.

MARK 4:35-5:43

Theme: "The Right Approach"

1. *When* **should we approach the Lord?**

   • When threatening circumstances engender fear within us (4:35-41).

   • Whenever we are engaged in some form of spiritual warfare or are susceptible to the destructive influence of the devil (5:1-20).

   • Whenever we are burdened for someone we love, as Jairus did (5:21-24).

- Or, like the woman with a physical ailment, whenever we have exhausted all other alternatives (5:25-34).

2. *How* should we approach the Lord? The characters in Mark 4:35-5:43 demonstrated the following attitudes: humility, boldness, trust and lack of concern over what others thought.

   - Their tendency to throw themselves at His feet (5:6, 22, 33) revealed humility.

   - The disciples' interruption of Jesus' sleep (4:38) as well as Jairus' and the woman's interruption of His trek over land (5:22, 27) demonstrated boldness as well as trust. They would not have interrupted Jesus had they no faith in His ability to intervene.

   - Their appeal in the midst of crowds indicated that they were not concerned about what others thought (5:21-22, 24-27).

   The fact that the characters approached Jesus at all suggests that they believed He could intervene and reverse their circumstances. Their faith revealed itself in their approach to the Lord.

3. *Why* should we approach the Lord? Mark 4:35-5:43 unveils characteristics about Jesus that should prompt us to take our needs to Him. He is capable and caring. He exerts authority over:

   - nature (4:35-41),
   - Satan (5:1-20),

- disease (5:25-34) and
- death (5:35-43).

The more familiar we are with Jesus' power and compassion, the more likely we are to approach Him with our problems. Our faith may seem weak at times, but the object of our faith—Jesus Christ—is always strong.

Personalizing the Passage

The characters in Mark 5 experienced hindrances to their faith in Christ. Despite those obstacles they demonstrated in observable ways that they trusted Him. They had heard and/or observed things about Jesus that engendered a measure of faith in Him and that prompted them to approach Him with their needs. Reflect on what you have read and apply it to your own life with the aid of these incomplete sentences:

- My capacity to trust Christ from day to day is sometimes hindered by _____

_____

_____

- One thing I've learned about Jesus—from Scripture as well as my own spiritual pilgrimage—that motivates me to trust Him with my needs is _____

_____

_____

- One way Jesus has worked in my life to test my trust level is _____

  _____

  _____

- The insight concerning faith in Mark 5 that impresses me most is _____

  _____

  _____

Memorizing Scripture

Memorize Psalm 55:22: "Cast your burden upon the LORD and He will sustain you; He will never allow the righteous to be shaken." As you concentrate on this verse, recall how the burdened individuals in Mark 5 applied it.

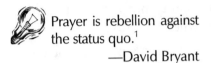

Prayer is rebellion against
the status quo.[1]
    —David Bryant

The Test of Praying Distinctively

Above a log-stuffed, crackling fireplace in the home of a Christian layman hangs the following sobering remark:

> If your heart is cold,
> my fire cannot warm it.[2]

What are some telltale signs that a believer's heart is growing cold? Perhaps the most obvious indicator is an anemic prayer life. Infrequent communication cools any relationship. You know that if you did not talk to your spouse or roommate for weeks, the temperature of that relationship would plunge below freezing. Similarly, if you stay out of contact with the Lord, your heart will grow cold.

One way to deepen your faith and fan the flames of your relationship with the Lord is through consistent communication with Him. This chapter serves as a thermostat to help regulate the climate of your walk with God. You will delve into Jesus' teaching on prayer to find the answers to these questions:

- What are some inappropriate approaches to prayer?

- What attitudes and motivations should characterize us when we pray?

- What guidelines did Jesus provide for the content of our prayers?

The answers are couched in what Jesus taught and modeled about prayer in Matthew 6:5-13. To turn up the heat in your own heart, read the passage and proceed to the Bible study exercises that follow.

Passage Background

What we glean about prayer from Matthew 6:5-13 is part of a larger section of Scripture called "The Sermon on the Mount." In Matthew 5-7, Jesus outlines traits, attitudes and behaviors that should distinguish His followers. Put simply, the theme of these Bible chapters is "Christians are different." For instance, a Christian's righteousness is more exacting than that of the Pharisees' since it incorporates motives and thoughts, not just external conduct. The law denounced the act of adultery, but Jesus added a prohibition against lust, which He called adultery of the heart (5:27-28). A Christian's love is broader, since it targets enemies as well as friends (5:43-47). And when the topic turned to acts of devotion—such as giving, praying and fasting—Jesus cited attitudes and behaviors that should distinguish His followers from hypocrites and devotees of other religions (6:1-15).

Now set your scope once again on Matthew 6:5-13.

Motivations for Prayer

Q Three times in Matthew 6:5-7 Jesus prefaced comments with the phrase "*when* you pray" or "*when* you are praying." **What did Jesus' use of the term "when" suggest about prayer?**

A _____

_____

Q According to Matthew 6:5-7 what inappropriate approaches to prayer did Jesus condemn?

A _____

_____

Q What specific type of praying did Jesus advocate?

A _____

_____

Q What positive motivations for praying can you find in Matthew 6:6-8? (Note what Jesus' words imply, not merely what He stated.)

A _____

_____

Jesus' use of "when" shows that He expects His followers to pray. As far as He is concerned, prayer is a normal occurrence in the life of someone who has received forgiveness from their sins. A follower who consistently prays is not an exceptional Christian. Rather, he is a *normal* Christian.

He warned against exhibitionism—praying in public with the intent to impress other people (6:5). Jesus also condemned mindless or superficial praying. The phrase "meaningless repetition" or "babbling like pagans" (NIV) in Matthew 6:7 literally means "to babble empty phrases." Jesus cited the negative habit of Gentiles who tried to impress their gods with a list of words recited on a rote level, rather than from the heart. In contrast to exhibitionism and mechanical repetitions, Jesus encouraged private prayer with an audience of One: God the Father (6:6).

What *should* prompt us to pray includes the promise of rewards to whoever approaches the Lord appropriately (6:6), the personal concern that God has for us—as implied by Jesus' use of the term "Father" (6:6, 8)—and the fact that God is aware of our needs even before we approach Him (6:8).

Guidelines for Prayer

In Matthew 6:9-13 the focus shifts from attitudes and motivations that prompt our prayers to the content of those prayers. Jesus provided a "model" prayer to serve as a framework for our conversations with God the Father. Examine the words of His prayer closely.

Q What does the opening sentence in Jesus' prayer (6:9) tell us about God?

A _____

_____

Q Why is a focus on God and His attributes an appropriate introduction to our own prayers?

A _____

_____

Q In Matthew 6:10-13, what specific concerns did Jesus mention? (Identify a different type of prayer, or content guideline, for each of the verses.)

A _____

_____

According to Jesus' model prayer, guidelines for our conversations with God include:

- Starting with an acknowledgment of who God is, citing one or more of His attributes (6:9).

- Making God's concerns a top priority, including intercession for His work in the world and fulfillment of His will on earth (6:10).

- Requesting provision for personal needs (6:11).

- Confessing sin (6:12).

- Seeking His assistance in daily spiritual warfare, particularly during bouts with temptation (6:13).

In Matthew 6:9, "Our Father" encourages awareness of God's parental concern. The phrase "who is in heaven" refers not only to the place of God's abode, but also implies the sovereign control of God over the affairs of man. "Hallowed be Your name" is a reference to the holiness and distinctiveness of God in comparison to His creatures.

Beginning a conversation with God with a focus on His specific attributes also characterized Jesus' prayer in Gethsemane (Mark 14:36) and Nehemiah's intercession for people in Jerusalem (Nehemiah 1:5). Jesus' references to "Your kingdom" and "Your will" are a reminder to pray about things closest to God's heart, such as world evangelization. Interceding for any aspect of God's work in the world—or "kingdom business"—is a valid application of this guideline.

Jesus' appeal for "daily bread" (Matthew 6:11) is a green light for petitionary prayer. This type of prayer "remains primary throughout our lives because we are forever dependent upon God."[3] Because Jesus unabashedly recommends petition, asking God to supply a need is *not* a lower, or less spiritual, form of prayer.

Jesus indicated that God the Father "knows what you need, *before* you ask Him" (6:8, emphasis added). Why should we ask for things that God already knows we need? Because God likes to be asked! "We like our children to ask us for things that we already know they need because the very asking enhances and deepens the relationship. . . . Love . . . wants to be asked for what it longs to give."[4]

We can apply Jesus' emphasis on seeking forgiveness (6:12) because His death on the cross made fellowship with God possible (Romans 5:8-11). To "confess" means "to agree with God" concerning the heinous nature of sin. When a Christian sins, his eternal status as a member of God's family is not threatened. The sin does, however, breach the Christian's fellowship with God and spawns painful consequences. The most quoted verse in the Bible on confession was directed to believers, not to the unchurched: "If we confess our sins, He is faithful and righteous to forgive us our sins and to cleanse us from all unrighteousness" (1 John 1:9).

Jesus taught that prayer is a supplement to the written Word in our warfare against temptation (Matthew 6:13). The phrase "deliver us from evil" may refer to evil influences in general or to Satan in particular. The word "evil" in this context can also be translated "the evil one." Jesus' intercession for His core disciples included, "keep them from the evil one" (John 17:15). And undoubtedly, one of the weapons of warfare Paul had in mind was prayer: "For though we walk in the flesh, we do not war according to the flesh, for the weapons of our warfare are not of the flesh, but divinely powerful for the destruction of fortresses" (2 Corinthians 10:3-4).

Your Practice of Prayer

Mull over what you have learned from Matthew 6:5-13 in view of your own practice of prayer.

Q The most helpful insight I gleaned from Jesus' teaching on prayer (6:5-8) is:

A _____

_____

_____

Jesus promoted *secret prayer* (6:6), implying that you need a special place free of interruptions and distractions.

Q Describe a time of day, as well as a location, where you can secretly meet with the Lord on a regular basis.

A _____

_____

The Lord discouraged *mindless praying* (6:7)— mechanical repetitions that do not spring from deep thought or passion.

Q What are some things you can do before or during prayer times to engage your mind—to minimize the likelihood that you will use meaningless repetition?

A _____

_____

_____

Q Based on your analysis of Jesus' model in Matthew 6:9-13, how should the content of your prayers change?

A _____

_____

_____

Jesus prayed, "*Your* kingdom come, *Your* will be done, on earth as it is in heaven" (6:10, emphasis added). To mirror Jesus' concern for the advancement of God's kingdom requires intercession for strategic work done on His behalf.

Q What Christian organizations and workers can you pray for more often?

A _____

_____

_____

Memorizing Scripture

Matthew 6:6 teems with insights. The phrase "*when* you pray" (emphasis added) reveals that Jesus expects you to communicate with God the Father. Phrases such as "your inner room," "close your door" and "in secret" show that private prayer is a top priority in Jesus' thinking. And the fact that "Your Father . . . will reward you" is a clear promise that God will respond to your prayers. Commit Matthew 6:6 to memory as a way to remind yourself of these truths.

Pressure is inevitable. Growth is not.

CHAPTER FIVE

The Test of Pressure

Q *Pressure.* **What do you associate with that term?** Right now, jot down what (or who) comes to mind when you consider that word:

A _____

_____

_____

Not even Jesus Christ was immune to pressure. During His time on earth He knew what it was like to feel the press of opposition and undesirable circumstances. Though He never sinned, He experienced grief and distress—even a temporary sense of alienation from God the Father.

Let us delve into Mark 14:32-42, which exposes Jesus' vulnerability to pressure. It is a text that reveals how He handled pressure and offers timeless insights on responding appropriately to our own gut-wrenching experiences.

Soak up every word of Mark 14:32-42 as if your stability under pressure depended on it—because it does.

Passage Background

Jesus' agony in Gethsemane occurred on Thursday evening of what we call "Passion Week"—the night prior to His crucifixion. The narrative in Mark 14:32-42 is sandwiched between His prophecy of the disciples' desertion (14:27-31) and its fulfillment (14:50). The term "Gethsemane" means "oil press," referring to the olive presses that dotted the landscape. This plot of land on the Mount of Olives was a familiar rendevous point for Jesus and His close band of followers.

The text offers a close look at Jesus' aloneness as He faced the pressure of the cross. He knew that His crucifixion was impending. After Peter had identified Jesus as the Messiah (8:29), Jesus began referring to His ultimate rejection and death (8:31). When Jesus prayed, "remove this cup from Me" (14:36), He was referring to the chalice of death—to God's wrath against sin—that He would take from the Father's hand in fulfillment of His earthly mission. In the Old Testament, the metaphor of a cup was used to represent the judgment of God poured out on sinners (Jeremiah 25:15; 49:12). Jesus would soon bear the judgment of sin that we deserve, as indicated in Second Corinthians 5:21: "He made Him who knew no sin to be sin on our behalf, so that we might become the righteousness of God in Him."

What caused Jesus' pressure was not primarily the prospects of crucifixion. Though He anticipated the tortuous physical pain associated with this barbaric means of capital punishment, He endured greater emotional and psychological distress. Remember that Jesus Christ had existed before the incarnation as a member of the Trinity. Never before had He experienced a second of separation or alienation from God the Father. He knew that when He hung on the cross He would be separated from God the Father for the first time in all eternity. God would have to forsake Him and let His Son experience the death *we* deserve for sin. Jesus' cry of anguish from the cross reflects the emotional trauma that began in earnest during the episode in Gethsemane: "MY GOD, MY GOD, WHY HAVE YOU FORSAKEN ME?" (Mark 15:34).

It is *not* likely that Jesus took with Him the inner core of disciples—Peter, James and John—because He needed their companionship during a stressful hour. They offered Him no help at all. Jesus separated Himself from the three when He prayed (14:35). And despite Jesus' encouragement for them to pray also, they kept falling asleep (14:37, 40, 41). Jesus told them to pray not for Him, but that *they* would "not come into temptation" (14:38). Jesus probably wanted to wean these beloved disciples from their pride and self-sufficiency. Peter had vowed to be loyal (14:29-31). James and John had insisted that they could "drink the cup" along with Jesus (10:38-39), while at the same time requesting a privileged status in Jesus' eventual kingdom (10:37). Jesus knew that their future effectiveness hinged on their humility and their daily de-

pendence on God's sufficiency rather than their
own. They needed to learn what Paul discovered a
few years later: "My grace is sufficient for you, for
power is perfected in weakness" (2 Corinthians
12:9).

For twenty-first century Christians, this text offers encouraging perspectives and identifies the
kind of praying that sustains us during pressure-
packed times.

Pressurized Prayers

To familiarize yourself with essential facts and
timeless principles, tackle the following questions:

Q What words/phrases from Mark 14:32-42
reveal Jesus' inner state?

A _____

_____

_____

Q Contrast Jesus' mind-set in 14:33-34 with
14:41-42. What apparent effect did the bouts
of prayer have on Him?

A _____

_____

_____

Q What words/phrases from the text describe the
three disciples during their time in the garden?

A _____

_____

_____

Q Focus on Jesus' prayer which is summarized
in 14:36. Keeping the context of 14:32-42
in mind, **How would you describe or characterize His praying?**

A _____

_____

_____

An analysis of the text reveals a prayer characterized by *persistence* (three separate bouts of sup-
plication which are seen in 14:35, 39 and 41),
privacy ("He went a little beyond them," 14:35),
honesty ("remove this cup from Me," 14:36) and
submissiveness ("Yet not what I will, but what
You will," 14:36).

Take a moment to evaluate the praying you do
during times of stress. On the scale provided on
the next page, determine the extent to which your
prayers are *persistent, private, honest* and *submis-
sive. (Note:* "Privacy" does not need to characterize every incident of praying. Other parts of
Scripture advocate public or group praying. But
Jesus' example suggests that secret, or private,
prayers should be one weapon in your arsenal in
anxiety-producing situations. Private wrestling
with the Lord is essential for complete honesty
and venting of emotions.)

My "prayers under pressure"
are marked by. . .

	NO					YES
Persistence:						
	0	1	2	3	4	5
Privacy:						
	0	1	2	3	4	5
Honesty:						
	0	1	2	3	4	5
Submissiveness:						
	0	1	2	3	4	5

Though the nature of Jesus' pressure was unique, He nonetheless can identify with your own experiences of stress and alienation.

Q What effect does knowing that Jesus identifies with the pressures you experience have on you?

A _____
_____
_____

Q Before answering the following question, read Hebrews 2:17-18 and 4:14-16. **What effect should awareness of Jesus' distress have on your relationship with Him?**

A _____
_____
_____

In Chapter 4—"The Test of Praying Distinctively"—which is based on Matthew 6:5-13, you examined Jesus' *teaching* on prayer. In Mark 14:32-42 you observe His *practice* of prayer. One instruction Jesus gave in Matthew 6:9 is to start prayers with a focus on specific attributes of God.

Q While He was in the Garden of Gethsemane how did Jesus "practice what He preached"? (In your answer, cite specific characteristics of God the Father implied in Mark 14:36.)

A _____

_____

When Jesus addressed God the Father as "Abba," He instituted a new element or emphasis to praying. The Aramaic word "Abba" was never used by first-century Jews as a means of addressing God. Since "Abba" was a familiar household word that a child would use with his or her earthly father, they thought such nomenclature would be disrespectful to the Lord. Jesus' use of the term connotes the intimacy of His relationship with the Father—the same intimacy *you* can enjoy. Such a personal address was an acknowledgment of God the Father's love and personal interest. God's love does not shield you from pressure but it can sustain you in the midst of it.

Each of the following Bible passages refers to your heavenly Father's sensitivity to you during adversity. After reading them, circle the verse that encourages you most, and serves as the strongest impetus for you to pray when pressured:

Psalm 4:1   Matthew 11:28-30
Psalm 27:1   Philippians 4:6-7
Psalm 68:19   First Peter 5:6-7

Another attribute of God the Father cited by Jesus is His power. "All things are possible for You," Jesus proclaimed (Mark 14:36). The verses that follow echo Jesus' emphasis on the power and sufficiency of God to intervene. Circle the passage that encourages you most:

Psalm 73:25-26   Luke 1:37
Jeremiah 32:17, 27   Ephesians 3:20-21

Because Jesus dreaded His impending separation from—and abandonment by—God the Father, He asked for a way to bypass the cross. "Remove this cup from Me," He cried (Mark 14:36). Yet seconds after venting His distress, Jesus submitted wholeheartedly to the Father's redemptive plan, asserting, "Yet not what I will, but what You will" (14:36). Jesus demonstrated a fundamental means of coping with stress as a Christian: *Yield to the known will of God no matter how unpleasant it seems.* Any temporary adversity that obedience causes will be offset by future joy and reward. Hebrews 12:2 describes Jesus' attitude after submitting to the inevitability of the cross: "Who for the joy set before Him endured the cross, despising the shame, and has sat down at the right hand of the throne of God." Clearly Jesus' prayers in Gethsemane relieved

Him of the pressure that racked His insides. What "praying under pressure" did for Jesus, it can do for you.

Q Describe a time in your experience, or in the life of someone you know, when a failure to submit to God's clearly revealed will magnified rather than reduced pressure.

A _____

_____

_____

Q Now describe a time in your life, or the life of someone you know, when obedience to God's will ultimately alleviated pressure, even when the idea of obeying appeared unpleasant.

A _____

_____

_____

Memorizing Scripture

When pressure deflates you and leaves you reeling, withdrawing a Bible verse from your memory bank can buoy your spirits. Psalm 73:26 reminds you that it's OK to feel weak—because *He* is strong. Be ready to recite the verse aloud when your discipleship group meets.

CHAPTER SIX

The Test of Personal Pain

Wouldn't it be great if you accidently whacked your thumb with a hammer, and it didn't throb? If you burned your palm on a scalding pot handle, yet you didn't feel a thing? If you fell off the roof of your house, landing with a thud on your arm, without experiencing one iota of pain?

No, it wouldn't.

Just ask Bob and Christine Waters from Great Britain. Their three children were born with one of the world's rarest physical maladies: *congenital analgia*, or insensitivity to pain. Rather than a cause for celebration, it is a curse. When the kids were toddlers, they constantly injured themselves without realizing it. Before the kids reached the age of three, they had bit off the tips of their fingers and tongues, scarred themselves with cuts, burned their hands severely and broken numerous bones. Before one girl reached two years old, she broke her right leg five times. The youngest child suffered from chronic nosebleeds, a result of constantly banging her face on the floor and walls. Bob and Christine learned the hard way that *pain is a friend, not a foe*. It is a built-in means of warning us and protecting us from more severe physical calamities.[2]

Pain is not necessarily an enemy in the spiritual realm, either. No one gets giddy about it, but the potential benefits of affliction often outweigh the unpleasantness.

Perry and Sandra Downs understand the nature of pain, as well as its advantages. They have cared for more than twenty physically, mentally or emotionally handicapped children over the years. Their pain includes the heart-wrenching experience of eventually giving up long-term foster kids whom they have grown to love. According to Perry,

> So much of the church wants to deny or avoid pain as if it's never God's will. They fail to realize that we grow through pain, that suffering has a redemptive quality. I think it's a really important aspect of spiritual growth that many times is denied.[3]

Gaining God's perspective on pain is integral to passing the faith test that it poses. A passage providing God's outlook on the subject is Second Corinthians 1:1-11. You will not encounter glib bromides that promise relief from painful experiences in this passage. You will, however, discover some potential benefits of suffering and identify resources to reas-

sure and sustain you when pain pierces either your
body or your heart.

Passage Background

Over a two-year period the apostle Paul discipled
the converts of the church he had planted in Cor-
inth during his second missionary journey. After
that time, he left for Ephesus, where he wrote the
letter known as First Corinthians. In that letter he
confronted problems which were surfacing in the
church, such as a spirit of competition and sexual
immorality. Titus delivered Paul's letter while Paul
shifted his location to Philippi. Titus eventually
joined Paul in Philippi, giving the apostle a "good
news-bad news" scenario about the church in Cor-
inth. The good news was that the majority of church
members had received Paul's letter with a teachable
spirit and had repented of the sins Paul had addressed. The bad news was that a minority were being influenced by false prophets who attacked Paul's
credentials as an apostle. As a result of Titus' mixed
report, Paul penned Second Corinthians, perhaps
Paul's most autobiographical letter. His intent was
to defend the message of the gospel as well as his
own apostleship. His defense began in chapter 1
with references to the suffering he had endured for
the cause of Christ.

Reality of Pain

Read Second Corinthians 1:1-11 carefully.

What words/phrases from the text denote suffering of some sort in the life experiences of Paul?

A _____

_____

_____

In the introduction to this letter, Paul did not get specific about his personal affliction. But he did refer in general terms to "our affliction" (1:4), to the "sufferings of Christ . . . [which] are ours in abundance" (1:5) and to "sufferings" (1:6-7). Also, he mentioned the "affliction which came to us in Asia" (1:8), which resulted in despair that sapped Paul's strength. Later in Second Corinthians, Paul pinpointed his affliction in more specific terms.

 Digest the experiences cited in Second Corinthians 11:23-28. **What effect would this list of afflictions have had on those who were doubting Paul's right to lead them as an apostle?**

A _____

_____

_____

Paul's painful experience is a microcosm of a broader biblical theme: *God's people are not immune to suffering.* In fact, propagating the gospel often incites opposition and results in some sort of affliction. What follows are only a few of the Scripture texts that offer a realistic view on the inevitability of pain during our earthly pilgrimage.

Q In a few words, summarize what each reference says about pain:

A Matthew 5:44-45 _____

_____

A Second Timothy 3:10-12 _____

_____

A James 1:2-4 _____

_____

In his classic devotional book, *Knowing God*, James I. Packer discusses the inevitability of pain in a broken world. He opposes the idea that accepting Christ means a respite from problems. In reference to the joyful, positive differences that may stem initially from conversion, he says:

> . . . it is possible so to stress them, and so to play down the rougher side of the Christian life—the daily chastening, the endless war with sin and Satan, the periodic walk in darkness—as to give the impression that normal Christian living is a perfect bed of roses, a state of affairs in which everything in the garden is lovely all the time, and problems no longer exist—or, if they come, they have only to be taken to the throne of grace, and they will melt away at once. This is to suggest that the world, the flesh, and the devil, will give a man no serious trouble once he is a Christian; nor will his circumstances and personal relationships ever be a problem to him; nor will he ever

be a problem to himself. Such suggestions are mischievous, however, because they are false.[4]

Later in the same chapter, Packer emphasizes how painful experiences are a tool in God's hand, a means He uses to accomplish the purposes of Christlikeness in the lives of His children:

> The reason why the Bible spends so much of its time reiterating that God is a strong rock, a firm defense, and a sure refuge and help for the weak, is that God spends so much of His time bringing home to us that we are weak, both mentally and morally, and dare not trust ourselves to find, or to follow, the right road. . . . God wants us to feel that our way through life is rough and perplexing, so that we may learn thankfully to lean on Him. Therefore He takes steps to drive us out of self-confidence to trust in Himself. . . .[5]

Some believers cling to a soft, unrealistic view of life as a Christian, expecting to experience on earth all the bliss and stress-free existence that God only promised for heaven.

 How do such persons tend to react when confronted by a problem or situation they can't handle?

A _____

_____

_____

The first point to take from Second Corinthians 1:1-11 is this: *We need a realistic perspective on the reality of pain.*

Reassurance during Pain

Q Look again at Second Corinthians 1:1-11. Jot down any words/phrases in this passage that reveal God's sensitivity to Paul's pain, or God's intervention to alleviate Paul's affliction:

A _____

_____

_____

_____

_____

Paul labeled Him "the Father of mercies and God of all comfort" (1:3). God had comforted Paul during his afflictions (1:4-7). God used Paul's pain to wean him of self-sufficiency and to deepen his faith (1:9). God intervened and "delivered us from so great a peril of death" (1:10).

A specific comment Paul made deserves closer inspection. He referred to "the sufferings of Christ," and the abundant comfort he found "through Christ" (1:5). Evidently, knowing Jesus Christ had suffered reassured Paul.

Q Turn to Hebrews 4:14-16. **When you are hurting, what effect should awareness of Christ's own suffering have on you?**

A _____

_____

_____

The character of God also assured Paul during troubling times. Paul viewed God as a "Father" who had a parental concern for him (2 Corinthians 1:3). Despite his suffering, Paul described God as merciful and comforting (1:3). Additional assurance came from the promise of a future bodily resurrection and a reservation in heaven. Paul's "eternal perspective" enabled him to endure painful times with optimism. He eagerly anticipated the "redemption of [his] body" (Romans 8:23). Paul had told the Corinthian church, "If we have hoped in Christ in this life only, we are of all men most to be pitied" (1 Corinthians 15:19). What kept Paul going in ministry was the eventual gift of an "imperishable body" (15:35-58).

The Lord does not shield you from all pain but He does reassure you in the here-and-now through His character, in addition to the promise of eternal life with Him.

Resources during Pain

In Second Corinthians 1:1-11, Paul suggests two distinct resources that he tapped into during painful times. The divine resources he alluded to answer the question, *How does God comfort us when we're hurting?*

The first resource sustaining Paul is implied in his references to divine comfort. Six separate times in 1:3-7 Paul mentioned the comfort of God the Father or Jesus Christ.

The teachings of Jesus Christ Himself enhance our understanding of Paul's experience.

 Mull over John 14:16-17, 26. **What is the channel for divine comfort available to Christians today?**

 _____

_____

In a monologue to encourage His followers over His impending physical departure, Jesus asserted that the _Holy Spirit_ would be given as a continual form of divine presence. Jesus used the term "Helper" or "Comforter" (LB) to describe the Holy Spirit. The word is the noun form of the Greek verb "to encourage." Its literal meaning is "one who comes alongside." When pain envelops you, the Holy Spirit can remind you of God's promises, instill you with an eternal perspective on a temporary setback and cultivate joy within you that coexists with the pain.

 Describe a painful experience from your past when you experienced the Holy Spirit's comfort.

 _____

_____

The second resource Paul mentioned is one of the means the Spirit employs to comfort you. Check out Second Corinthians 1:11.

 What words in this verse suggest a tangible resource of sustenance for Paul?

A _____

_____

_____

The Corinthians' prayers demonstrated the authenticity of the fellowship Paul enjoyed with them. Similarly, he relied on prayers offered by the Philippians (Philippians 1:19) and the Ephesians (Ephesians 6:19). One way in which the Lord wants to strengthen you during pain is through the presence and ministry of other Christians. They can serve as your "burden bearers" (Galatians 6:2) and your teachers (Colossians 3:16). They may facilitate your spiritual growth through warnings (Romans 15:14) and exhortations to action (Hebrews 10:24). The forms fellowship takes vary, but here is the bottom line: _Christians are interdependent people who need each other. God never meant for anyone in His family to deal with pain alone._

 Describe a time when you either received comfort from another Christian or extended it to a hurting person.

A _____

_____

_____

Results of Pain

Though no one extends a special invitation to painful experiences, their unannounced visits may yield positive results. Scan Second Corinthians 1:3- 9 again.

Q Locate two positive effects of Paul's suffering:

A Based on 1:3-7: _____

_____

A Based on 1:9: _____

_____

First, *Paul's pain—and the subsequent experience of divine comfort—expanded his capacity to encourage others who hurt.* What was the ultimate outcome of Paul's suffering and God's extension of comfort to him? Paul's own words answer the question: "that we may be able to comfort those who are in any affliction with the comfort with which we ourselves are comforted by God" (2 Corinthians 1:4).

Here's a maxim that captures, in streamlined fashion, this potential benefit of pain: *Your greatest area of usefulness to God may stem from your greatest area of pain.*

People sustained by God during painful experiences make the best comforters. They know that not all affliction is a direct consequence of sin. Their identification with the other person's pain increases their sensitivity and engenders within them a proclivity to listening. Their firsthand experience of divine comfort enables them to offer hope without minimizing the reality of the person's ordeal.

Describe a time when your own ministry of comfort to someone was prompted by your own grief, or when you received comfort from another believer who could identify:

A _____

_____

_____

Second, *Paul's trials weaned him from a self-sufficient spirit.* He realized his limitations and the absolute necessity of relying on God from day to day. Perhaps Proverbs 3:5, "Trust in the LORD with all your heart and do not lean on your own understanding" surfaced in Paul's mind as he wrote Second Corinthians 1:9. Only through pain did Paul learn that when he was at wit's end, he was at the beginning of God's wisdom. When no other recourse presented itself, Paul began to cleave to Him in a way that would never have happened otherwise.

Indelible Impressions

 Which "perspective on pain" rooted in Second Corinthians 1:3-11 means most to you right now? Why?

A _____

_____

_____

Memorizing Scripture

To serve as a permanent reminder of this Bible study, memorize Second Corinthians 1:3-4. These verses will remind you of God's willingness to comfort and the potential expansion of your ministry to hurting people.

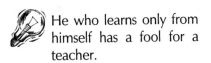 He who learns only from himself has a fool for a teacher.

CHAPTER SEVEN

The Test of Responding to Criticism

A well-known Christian author gives the following account of a conversation with a friend:

I have often told the story of my special friend, Philip Armstrong, a missionary leader lost in a plane crash in Alaska. We were walking along a Japanese street when I made a derogatory comment about a mutual acquaintance. "Gordon," Armstrong immediately said, "a man of God would not say such a thing about another person." I was exposed and knew it. He was right. The rebuke stung, and I lived with its pain for many days afterward. But I will always be thankful for that rebuke, painful as it was, because I hear those words every time I am about to embarrass myself with a needless comment about another person. That was a rebuke that forced me to grow.[1]

Reproof, or criticism, is a type of faith test. Even when the person who criticizes us is an admired person, their words hurt. Responding in a mature manner requires faith. *Can we actually trust God to assist us spiritually through the words of others—especially when they are so imperfect themselves?* How we respond to critics is a prime indicator of our character and a clear indicator of the extent of our faith.

Reprovers are not on target every time. And they don't always come across like honor graduates from the school of social etiquette. However, God's Word insists on an attitude of interdependence among Christians and exalts a teachable spirit that listens to others' input. Instead of muttering, "Pardon me for living!" when we receive unsolicited advice or reproof, Scripture tells us to tune in to their sound waves.

To help you pass the test posed by critics, the following pages shuttle you to two portions of Scripture: a New Testament case study featuring a teachable response to advice and the book of Proverbs, which devotes a whopping amount of space to receiving counsel and reproof. In addition to hard-hitting biblical insights, you will receive practical tips for responding to a critic, plus guidelines for ferreting out unfair criticism from the spiritually constructive variety.

Portrait of Accountability

Apollos was the Ph.D. of first-century Christian workers. He grew up in Alexandria, the cultural and educational capital of ancient Egypt, where he received a top-notch education in Greek classical literature and the Jewish Scripture.

Acts 18:24-28 describes the time Apollos entered the city of Ephesus. There he assisted in the church work already started by Paul and a lay married couple named Aquila and Priscilla. Before you scrutinize this portrait of accountability, rivet this point deeply into your mind: Apollos was *not* guilty of inaccurate or erroneous teaching. The passage clearly states that what he knew, he taught accurately. But despite his scholar's grasp of the Old Testament, there were gaps in his knowledge about Jesus. No doubt he was convinced that Jesus was the Messiah but he was not familiar with all the details concerning Christ's earthly ministry, death and resurrection.

Keeping that backdrop in mind, familiarize yourself with Acts 18:24-28 and answer the following questions:

Q What were Apollos' credentials, competencies and character traits? List words/phrases directly from the text which show his assets or advantages.

A _____

_____

_____

Q Acts 18:27-28 describes Apollos' subsequent ministry in Achaia. What do these verses imply about Apollos' reaction to Priscilla and Aquila's input?

A _____

_____

_____

Q What words from 18:27-28 suggest that Priscilla and Aquila's input enhanced Apollos' service?

A _____

_____

_____

Q Previously, you listed Apollos' assets and abilities. Why do personal strengths and credentials often hinder one's responsiveness to counsel or criticism?

A _____

_____

_____

   Ironically, ministry capacities and past usefulness to God are potential stumbling blocks to teachability. If pride develops, a teachable spirit exits (see Chapter 9 which is entitled "The Test of Prosperity"). Apollos never allowed the bite of pride to spread its deadly venom into his bloodstream. Though his overall knowledge and public abilities probably ran proverbial circles around Aquila and Priscilla, he still submitted to their input. He realized that all service is, in some form, a team effort. He knew that no individual servant ever has it all together.

Calling All Critics

   A recurring theme in the book of Proverbs is responsiveness to counselors and critics. We have

selected a few of the most penetrating references
for your consideration:

Proverbs 9:8-9   Proverbs 15:5, 31-33
Proverbs 10:17   Proverbs 17:10
Proverbs 12:1, 15   Proverbs 27:17
Proverbs 13:18   Proverbs 29:1

Q List words from these verses that describe either a person who resists criticism or the negative consequences of resisting others' input.

A _____

_____

_____

_____

_____

Q List words/phrases directly from the verses that describe either a person who accepts criticism or the positive results of listening to others' input:

A _____

_____

_____

_____

Q The specific Proverb advocating an openness to others' input that leaves the biggest impression on me is:

A

Because:

Not all criticism or counsel takes the form of rebuke. A rebuke is a sharp reprimand that implies we are wrong or off track and need to change course immediately. Several of the Proverbs you read clearly show the link between rebuke and spiritual growth. In *Restoring Your Spiritual Passion*, Gordon MacDonald nods in agreement:

> We all need truth-tellers, even if we don't really want them. . . . No one grows where truth is absent. No one is pushed *to be* and *to do* the best. . . . One solid rebuke is worth a hundred affirmations. Rebukes are the purifiers which keep spiritual passion clear and forceful. . . . Rebukes were and still are among my greatest learning moments. They set me free from things that otherwise would have destroyed my spiritual passion.[2]

Responsible Responses

Psalm 141:5 reads, "Let a righteous man strike me—it is a kindness; let him rebuke me—it is oil on my head. My head will not refuse it" (NIV). How can we cultivate that kind of attitude toward criticism? What are some useful techniques for accepting others' input in an Apollos-like manner? How can we distinguish fair from unfair criticism? To respond in a Proverbs-like manner, apply the tips that follow:

- *Pray.* Ask the Lord to cultivate within you a teachable rather than a defensive spirit. Ask for the discernment to determine what is accurate, and what is exaggerated, in the critic's observations. Gordon MacDonald's *Ordering Your Private World* offers this challenging anecdote:

  > Dawson Trotman, the founder of the Navigators, had a good method for handling all criticism directed at himself. No matter how unfair the criticism might seem to be, he would always take it into his prayer closet and in effect spread it before the Lord. Then he would say, "Lord, please show me the kernel of truth hidden in this criticism."[3]

- *Let the critic finish.* Even if you think his or her opinion is invalid, resist the urge to interrupt. When our egos are threatened, snapping back is almost as automatic as the reflex action that causes our eyes to blink when invaded by a foreign object. Tuck Proverbs 29:11 into your memory: "A fool always loses his temper, but a wise man holds it back." Before you respond to criticism ask, "Is there anything else?" Let the person know you are listening by maintaining good eye contact with him.

- *To insure that you understand the complaint, restate or paraphrase the critic's observations.*

Say something like, "I want to make sure I'm hearing you right. You are saying that. . . ." Sometimes we defend ourselves against charges that were never made. Checking for understanding can also keep you from fostering an exaggerated perception of a person's criticism. If someone says you were thoughtless on one occasion, he is not necessarily labeling you an insensitive dolt.

- *If an apology is in order, be big enough to do it quickly.* Putting it off only makes it harder to say you're sorry. Remember that *truth doesn't hurt—unless it ought to!* Also realize that it is difficult for most people to confront others. Set your critic at ease by thanking him for caring enough to approach you.

- *If you are not immediately convinced the critic is correct, give yourself time to mull things over with a standard reply such as, "You could be right. I'll think about what you said."* By saying this, you aren't conceding anything—you are telling the critic that you are taking his input seriously. Such a response also keeps you from rash or thoughtless reaction. "Do you see a man who is hasty in his words? There is more hope for a fool than for him" (Proverbs 29:20). Taking time to mull things over gives you time to simmer down and evaluate the criticism more objectively.

- *To help you weigh the accuracy of a criticism, follow these steps:* (1) *Consider the source.* Ponder such questions as: Is the critic a person of integrity? Does he or she have a history of loyalty? Is the person gaining anything by the criticism, or is there genuine concern about me or somebody else I've hurt? The more respect you have for the person, the more likely he is on target with the criticism. (2) *Consider the number of people who have offered the same criticism.* When two or more folks volunteer the same painful observation, chances are their comments should be heeded. (3) *Talk to someone whose opinion you respect and who knows you well.* Tell this person what the critic said. Then ask: "Do you have the same impression? Has this critic exposed something I need to work on? How should I respond?"

Critical Analysis

Here is a way to apply what you have learned about teachability and responding to criticism. This trek into your past can prepare you for your next encounter with a critic or advisor.

Q Think of a time within the past year when you were on the receiving end of what you would call a rebuke or some other form of critical feedback. Briefly describe the incident:

A _____

_____

_____

_____

Q When you first heard the critic's remarks,
how did you *feel*? Did you agree or disagree
with the feedback? Explain.

A _____

_____

_____

_____

_____

Q At the time, how did you *respond* to the criticism? What did you say to the critic?

A _____

_____

_____

_____

_____

Q Now that you have examined Scripture and
practical tips on the subject, what (if anything) would you change about your original reaction to the critic and the criticism?
Use insights from this chapter to write a de-
tailed analysis of your original response.

A _____

_____

_____

_____

_____

Memorizing Scripture

Memorizing Proverbs 17:10 can help to cultivate within you an openness to critics' opinions: "A rebuke goes deeper into one who has understanding than a hundred blows into a fool."

If we truly love people, we will desire for them more than is within our power to give them, and this will lead us to prayer. Intercession is a way of loving others.[1]

—Richard Foster

CHAPTER
EIGHT

The Test of Discouraging News

Have you ever received a letter from someone you love which contained news of an adversity he is facing? Perhaps it is a daughter in college who flunked her first algebra exam. A sister who has been diagnosed with cancer. A close friend who is disabled by chronic depression. Or perhaps you were informed of a revered Christian leader whose moral collapse destroyed his family and stained God's reputation.

Those kinds of circumstances pose a unique test of faith because you have less control over them. What happens to others and how they respond to their trial is often outside of your direct control.

If your faith in God has ever been challenged by discouraging news from another person or group, then you would probably identify with Nehemiah. While serving the king in Babylon, Nehemiah received disturbing news concerning the plight of his countrymen who had returned from captivity to Jerusalem. He responded to a situation out of his control by going to God, knowing He could alter the situation.

Examining Nehemiah's response to discouraging news will help you learn to pass similar faith tests of your own through the practice of intercessory prayer. On the pages that follow you will discover character traits that go hand-in-hand with the consistent practice of intercession. You will identify timeless elements of intercession that move God to action and will uncover practical measures some mature believers take to enhance their intercession.

Passage Background

As a disciplinary measure for Israel's idolatry, God employed the foreign power of Babylon to ransack Israel and deport most of the population. After a seventy-year exile, He permitted a remnant to return to Jerusalem and launch a rebuilding project. The Jews who returned to their homeland went in three separate companies. Ninety years prior to the events in the first chapter of Nehemiah, the first group went back to Jerusalem under the leadership of Zerubbabel. Around eighty years later, Ezra the scribe led a second entourage. As described in the second chapter of Nehemiah, Nehemiah led a third party to Jerusalem ten or twelve years after Ezra's arrival. Despite the ninety-year span of time since the first band of Jews had returned, it took the wise and strong leadership of Nehemiah to mobilize the Jews and rebuild the city wall. Prior to Nehemiah's administrative leadership, the remnant was discouraged, vulnerable to attack and the rubble of Jerusalem's gates and walls was a constant eyesore. Here is one commentator's take on why the status of the city gate and wall was so important:

> Walls and gates mean nothing to cities nowadays, but long ago, in the east, they meant almost everything. Those torn-down walls and gates left the inhabitants open to attack and plunder by vicious neighbors; and it is quite probable that Hanani's report to Nehemiah was made the more poignant by the fact that the citizens of Jerusalem had at that very time been suffering in this way from the deceitful and treacherous people who surrounded them.[2]

When the narrative of Nehemiah opens in Chapter 1, he is serving as a cupbearer to King Artaxerxes in the Persian court. Nehemiah's role was a lucrative one, indicating that he enjoyed the trust of the royal family. For instance, Nehemiah sampled all wine given to the king to forestall the possibility of assassination by poisoning.

As you examine Nehemiah's response to discouraging news in Chapter 1, remember that he did not initially plan to intervene by going to Jerusalem himself. His plan to supervise the construction project was planted in his heart by the Lord over a period of time.

Portrait of an Intercessor

Read Nehemiah 1:1-11 and respond to the questions that follow.

Q What news did Nehemiah receive about the Jewish remnant in Jerusalem? (1:2-3)

A _____

_____

_____

Nehemiah received news about their need because he asked the visitors from Judah for information (1:2).

Q What does Nehemiah's inquiry about the Jewish remnant teach us about the ministry of intercession?

A _____

_____

_____

Effective intercession stems from an awareness of specific needs. Like Nehemiah, we should take initiative to obtain the necessary information.

Q Give an example of how asking questions—or taking initiative to discover someone's needs—helps an intercessor.

A _____

_____

_____

Nehemiah wept, fasted and prayed over the plight of the people and of Jerusalem (1:4). **To what extent does pain or brokenness motivate intercessory prayer?**

A _____

_____

_____

Others' pain or adverse situations can bring us to the end of self-reliance and cause us to seek divine relief on their behalf.

Share a time when you entered into a period of intercession due to someone else's pain.

A _____

_____

_____

A summary of Nehemiah's prayer begins in 1:5. Carefully read 1:5-11 again. Jot down guidelines for the content of our prayers based on Nehemiah's example. To put it another way, **what did Nehemiah say and do during his prayer that should shape the content of *our* prayers?**

Here are catalysts for your thinking in response to this analytical assignment: note attributes of God Nehemiah cited, the use of first person plural pronouns such as "we" when referring to the nation's sin and his reference to promises God had made to Moses regarding Israel. Mull over the implications of these kind of facts for *our* prayers.

A _____

_____

_____

_____

_____

_____

_____

Guidelines for our prayer content gleaned from Nehemiah 1:5-11 include the following:

- *Begin times of prayer with a citation of one or more divine attributes.* In 1:5, Nehemiah launched his intercession with these words: "I beseech You, O LORD God of heaven, the great and awesome God, who preserves the covenant and lovingkindness for those who love Him." The rationale for concentrating on God's attributes is the effect it has on the person praying. Focusing on who God is serves as an impetus for prayer. We are more apt to persist in prayer if we believe we are addressing Someone with the willingness and the competence to intervene.

- *Before making a request, confess any known sin to the Lord* (1:6-7). Failure to acknowledge sin is a common reason for unanswered prayer. "If I regard wickedness in my heart, the Lord will not hear" (Psalm 66:18).

- *Be aware of God's timeless promises in His Word, which fuel intercession.* Nehemiah's prayer was prompted by promises previously delivered to Moses (Nehemiah 1:8-9). Jesus Himself linked the awareness of God's truth and the effectiveness of prayers: "If you abide in me, *and My words abide in you*, ask whatever you wish, and it will be done for you" (John 15:7, emphasis added).

 From his words/actions in Chapter 1, what else can you learn from Nehemiah about the ministry of intercession?

A _____

_____

_____

Nehemiah's example should prompt us to *approach God boldly.* Nehemiah's conversation with God revealed his dauntless approach. He reiterated, "I beseech You" (Nehemiah 1:5), "Let Your ear now be attentive" (1:6) and "I beseech You, may Your ear be attentive" (1:11). He demonstrated what the author of Hebrews told us to do centuries later: "Draw near with confidence to the throne of grace" (Hebrews 4:16).

Nehemiah also demonstrated the willingness to involve himself directly in the needs of those for whom he prayed. He said to the Lord, "Make Your servant successful today and grant him compassion before this man" (Nehemiah 1:11). At this point Nehemiah was already planning to approach the king for permission to go to Jerusalem and rebuild the ruins.

From the time Nehemiah started praying for the remnant (1:4), to the time he devised a plan and approached the king (2:1), was a period of four months.

Q What does that fact suggest about the ministry of intercession?

A _____

_____

_____

Intercession is clearly not a one-time event. A burdened heart keeps crying out to God, persisting in a plea for His intervention.

Your Practice of Intercession

Nehemiah was not satisfied with the status quo in Jerusalem. Think of a "status quo" in the life of an individual, family or group with which you are currently dissatisfied.

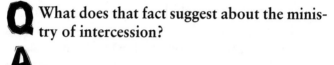 Rebel against this status quo *now* by interceding for the need of the person, family or group which came to mind. Summarize your prayer in the space below:

_____

_____

_____

_____

Q The insight about intercession from Nehemiah 1 that the Holy Spirit is impressing on you now is:

A _____

_____

_____

Q In response to needs or discouraging news about others, one way your prayers will change as a result of this study is:

A _____

_____

_____

Memorizing Scripture

To serve as an impetus for your intercession, memorize these words from First Samuel 12:23: "Far be it from me that I should sin against the LORD by ceasing to pray for you."

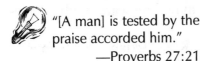
The Test of Prosperity

Years ago, before the procedure became politically incorrect, high school and college chemistry students were occasionally required to watch a frog boil. The teacher put the unsuspecting creature in a large beaker of cool water. Then he scooted a Bunsen burner beneath the beaker and ignited a very low flame. That small flame heated the water very slowly—several hundredths of a degree per second—so the water temperature escalated gradually. Class members would then check the beaker a couple of hours later and would find a dead frog—it boiled to death!

Here is the surprising part. Anyone who kept his eyes on the frog the whole time never saw the creature squirm or try to jump out of the water. The change occurred so slowly that the frog was never aware of it. He never realized that he was in any danger.

That gruesome demonstration is analogous to how gradually a person's attitudes and values can erode. Sin rarely destroys a person's life instantaneously. Rather, the change happens subtly, over a period of time. If we are not careful, we sud-

denly find ourselves in boiling water with no ave-
nue of escape.

What happened to King Uzziah is analogous to
what happens to a slow-boiled frog. At first
glance it looks like his fall from the pinnacle of
prestige to the quicksand of disgrace was sudden.
In the span of a few hours, he was tossed from the
Oval Office of Judah and branded a social out-
cast. But a closer investigation shows that the un-
derlying cause of his fall from power had been
welling up inside him for quite some time. The
flame of pride flickered in his heart and gradually
eroded his character. Then on one unfortunate
occasion, it permanently scarred his life.

Take the following story of King Uzziah to
heart and you will save yourself from a lot of hot
water. You will discover that he failed the most
rigorous test of faith that a Christian ever con-
fronts: *prosperity*. When God blesses you and ar-
ranges circumstances to expedite your success,
there is a tendency to forget Him. Failing this test
is not inevitable, but awareness of its challenge is a
prerequisite for a passing grade. Your look at
Uzziah's life will place the following truth deep in
your consciousness: *prosperity is a much stiffer
test of faith than adversity.*

Royal Achiever

To familiarize yourself with Uzziah's story, read
Second Chronicles 26. Note the "riches-to-rags"
nature of his personal circumstances. The questions

that follow will focus your attention on the most consequential facts and the conclusions they spawn.

Q What evidences of Uzziah's successful reign does 26:6-11 mention?

A _____

_____

_____

Q Now set your scope on 26:1-7. List all the words/phrases from your Bible that:

A Explain the reason for Uzziah's success:

_____

_____

_____

A Describe Uzziah's spiritual state early in his reign:

_____

_____

_____

Clearly, the explanation for the king's prosperous reign was _God_ (26:5, 7). The Lord honored Uzziah because "he did right in the sight of the LORD" (26:4) and "he continued to seek God" (26:5).

Q What conclusions can you derive from God's involvement in Uzziah's success?

A _____

_____

_____

Success is not inherently wrong. As Uzziah's early reign illustrates, God may even give various forms of prosperity to His people. What makes all the difference is one's attitude toward prosperity. Whether the arena is college grades, business, family relationships or personal evangelism, success may represent a direct answer to prayer. Just do not underestimate the vulnerability that accompanies even divine blessings. Apparently, that is what happened to Uzziah.

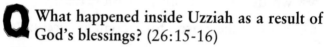 **What happened inside Uzziah as a result of God's blessings?** (26:15-16)

———————————————————————

———————————————————————

The text does not explain how it happened but it does suggest that Uzziah became addicted to the narcotic of self-importance. Arrogance penetrated a chink in the king's armor. After "his fame spread afar" (26:15), "his heart was . . . proud" (26:16). The term translated "proud" in verse 16 carries the idea of being "lifted up."

Uzziah's failing grade in response to success was not an isolated case in Scripture. Time and again, the nation of Israel faltered after receiving blessings from the hand of God. After God's chosen people captured fortified cities and took possession of a fertile landscape, "they ate, were filled and grew fat, and reveled in [God's] great goodness" (Nehemiah 9:25). What happened next? "They became disobedient and rebelled against [God], and cast [His] law behind their backs" (9:26). Prior to their enjoyment of the promised land, God had miraculously intervened by delivering them from Egypt and providing food in the wilderness. Yet "they forgot His deeds and His miracles that He had shown them" (Psalm 78:11). Whoever penned Proverbs 30:8-9 understood the inclination of the human heart to take credit for success: "Give me neither poverty nor riches; feed me with the food that is my portion, that I not be full and deny You and say, 'Who is the LORD?' Or that I not be in want and steal, and profane the name of my God."

Q Why is it helpful to be aware of the heart's propensity for pride?

A _____

_____

_____

Test Results

The last half of Second Chronicles 26 discloses events spawned by Uzziah's pride. Look again at Second Chronicles 26:16-18. He entered the temple of the Lord to burn incense on the altar. Then eighty priests tried unsuccessfully to restrain him.

Q What light does Numbers 16:39-40 shed on Uzziah's behavior?

A _____

_____

_____

Though Uzziah was engaged in a religious activity, he was blatantly disobedient to divine law. God had separated the functions of king and priests. Not even the political ruler could usurp the duties of a priest. Pride eroded Uzziah's values to the extent that he took God's Word flippantly.

Q **What manifestation of pride do you see in Uzziah's reaction to the priests?** (2 Chronicles 26:17-19)

A _____

_____

_____

Uzziah's prosperity resulted in fame, which spawned a spirit of self-sufficiency within him. His pride showed in rebellion against the Word of God, then in his refusal to accept reproof. He was not accountable to the spiritual leaders God had placed around him. If only he had heeded Proverbs 15:31-32: "He whose ear listens to the life-giving reproof will dwell among the wise. He who neglects discipline despises himself, but he who listens to reproof acquires understanding." Instead, he demonstrated the truth of Proverbs 29:1: "A man who hardens his neck after much reproof will suddenly be broken beyond remedy."

Q Reflect on Proverbs 16:18. **What happened to King Uzziah that illustrated the truth of that warning?**

A _____

_____

_____

Q Describe a contemporary example of the disastrous consequences of a proud, independent spirit within a Christian:

A _____

_____

_____

Test Preparation

Q In what ways has the Lord blessed you? Jot down several examples of success or areas of life in which God has prospered you. Do not merely think in material or vocational realms, but include blessings such as close-knit interpersonal relationships, ministry effectiveness, physical health and the accomplishments of your children.

A _____

_____

_____

_____

_____

_____

_____

Now ponder this question: **How can you avoid the deep-rooted human disposition toward conceit and forgetfulness of God?** Describe a few things you can do to defend against pride and pass the faith test posed by your blessings.

A _____

_____

_____

To avoid the human disposition toward conceit and forgetfulness of God, some believers dare to ask God to keep them humble. (That is a request He is not likely to ignore!) Others engage in concentrated prayers of gratitude for the blessings they receive. They do not put off thanking God for answered prayers, or for day-to-day attainments that are easy to take for granted. They are also quick to give God credit when they converse with others. Some defend their hearts against pride by asking a few trusted friends to hold them accountable and confront them when arrogance starts to show. Yet another strategy is to use a concordance and look up all the references to pride in the book of Proverbs. Such a topical study requires keeping an eye out for terms such as *arrogance, haughty, boasting* and *humble.* Soaking up what Scripture says about a proud spirit can keep your heart tender and less vulnerable to conceit. If the Proverbs project entices you, look for the causes of pride, the ways pride expresses itself in a person, its negative effects on relationships and how God feels about it.

Years ago, an ad produced by a sporting goods manufacturer was broadcast over television. The company was touting a tennis racket that a champion had used in the prestigious Wimbledon tournament. The ad showed the winner zigzagging all over the court, slapping the tennis ball across the net toward a befuddled opponent. Then an announcer's voice boasted, *"Our racket won Wimbledon!"*

Stop and think about the announcer's words. What a pompous and ridiculous claim! Millions across the world had watched the Wimbledon broadcasts and they thought all along that an American tennis player—not the racket—had won the tournament. Who deserved the sports page accolades, the victor's trophy, the hefty winner's purse? Did that racket win Wimbledon, with assistance from the player? Or did the player win Wimbledon with the racket's help?

Inflating our egos over abilities and successes is as foolish as the tennis racket demanding an interview with the press and lobbying for half the winner's purse. King Uzziah learned the hard way that the one who controls the racket should get the credit.

Memorizing Scripture

Hiding the second half of Isaiah 66:2 in your heart will help prevent pride from wedging its way in: "But to this one I will look, to him who is humble and contrite of spirit, and who trembles at My word."

When God gives us an or-
der, it is utterly impossible to say, "No, Lord" and mean
both words.[1]
—Robertson McQuilkin

The Test of an Unpleasant Task

When God calls, do you ever hang up on Him? That probably depends on what He says or what He tells you to do.

The primary way in which God phones in His expectations for His people is through biblical commands. When He divulges His will in imperative form, what He wants you to do is not up for debate. Things like marital fidelity and fudging on tax returns are not viable options for a Christian.

He also connects with you through the more subjective leading of the Holy Spirit. He may nudge you to give a portion of a bonus to a mission project, to write someone a letter of encouragement, to witness to an unchurched neighbor or to teach the junior high Sunday school class. Precise intentions of that sort aren't spelled out in Scripture. They are tailor-made expectations that He discloses to folks who sincerely want to please Him with their lives.

We would be remiss, however, if we did not point out a sobering secret of the Christian life: *not every assignment God gives you is enjoyable or agreeable.* Occasionally what He wants you to do is downright unpleasant, going against the grain of personal preference. But in the long run, obeying Him is always in your best interest. No one who does what the Lord says regrets it down the road. But if you are honest, once in a while He points in a direction that you do not want to go. That is a test of faith—with a capital "T"!

If He urges you to reach out to a difficult coworker, you may balk. Who knows how such a cranky person will react? If God impresses on you the need to disclose a dishonest practice by your supervisor, you may hesitate for fear of losing your job. If He wants you to confront a Christian friend who has wandered off course morally, your desire to stay in his favor may supercede what you know is right. Perhaps you are convinced God wants you on the mission field, yet the prospect of leaving family and friends—as well as raising financial support—frightens you.

If you can identify with any of those scenarios, you will appreciate meeting Jonah, who tried to circumvent the will of God for his life. Jonah was someone who at first failed the faith test posed by an unpleasant task but received a second chance to take it. He was someone whose story will remind you that God has good reasons for giving unpleasant assignments.

Assignment: Nineveh

Take a moment to skim the book of Jonah. This historical narrative consists of four short chapters, so a quick read will only take a few minutes. Then augment your grasp of the story with the following background information.

Background Information

According to Second Kings 14:25, Jonah lived in the northern kingdom of Israel, prophesying there during the reign of Jeroboam II (about 793-753 B.C.). The book of Jonah wastes no space getting to the plot. God told Jonah to visit Nineveh and warn the inhabitants of God's wrath if they didn't repent (1:2). Normally, prophets proclaimed God's message to the Jewish people, to jar them out of a state of complacency or to predict future actions of the Lord. This time, however, God assigned Jonah to a spot 500 miles from home, to a people group who were dreaded enemies of Israel. Nineveh was the capital of Assyria, inhabited by folks who had raided Israel in the past. It is even possible that Ninevites within earshot of Jonah's preaching had plundered Jonah's own relatives and friends.

Skeptics scoff at the episode featuring the prophet inside a fish for three days (Jonah 2), but the God who created natural laws is capable of skirting them occasionally in order to accomplish His purpose. If someone believes in the God of the Bible, it is logical for him to believe in supernatural deeds as a consequence. Belief in one miracle—creation of the world, Jesus' incarnation or His resurrection— should pry open our minds to the possibility of others. To believe in God, yet to doubt an incident such as the one described in Jonah 2 is intellectually inconsistent. Besides, Jesus Himself saluted the historical accuracy of Jonah. He compared His impending death and resurrection to Jonah's stay in the fish (Matthew 12:40). Questioning the historical accuracy of Jonah amounts to doubting Jesus' integrity.

Now it is time to determine how Jonah scored on the test of an unpleasant task. What you learn about the Lord and His plan will overshadow what you learn about the prophet.

The Fugitive

 Focus on Chapter 1 of Jonah. **How would you describe Jonah's reaction to God's commission?**

  _____

_____

_____

Jonah's behavior indicated that he viewed God's orders as distasteful. In fact, his destination, the Spanish seaport of Tarshish, was 2,000 miles in the opposite direction from Nineveh!

Read the historical backdrop in the "Assignment: Nineveh" section again (pages 108-110). **In twenty words or less, why was God's assigned task so galling to Jonah?**

A _____

_____

Although God's directives do not always involve a geographical relocation, what He asks of us occasionally causes inner turmoil similar to that of Jonah's.

Q When we try to flee God's presence or skirt His prescribed plan for us, what are some forms our avoidance takes?

A _____

_____

Means of avoidance or escape include becoming absorbed in work or leisure activities, claiming inadequacy when He clearly calls us to fulfill a particular ministry or compensating for a specific area of disobedience by engaging in "good deeds"—even church work—in an effort to relieve the conviction of sin. Yet all attempts to drown out the still small voice of God will prove as futile as Jonah's flight turned out to be.

Q What facts from Chapter 1 show that God did not abandon His plan for Jonah?

A _____

_____

Q Imagine: not even Jonah's defiance thwarted God's plan for Jonah's life. **What does His continued involvement with Jonah tell you about God?**

God does not allow His children to sin successfully.[2] He cared too much about Jonah, as well as
the people of Nineveh, to permit him to "sin successfully."

 In what ways does the Lord work today to
get the attention of His rebellious children?

Sometimes God gets our attention through a
tender conscience, stimulated by a biblical teaching or a friend's reproof. He may also employ
painful circumstances to provide a fresh perspective or to create more of an openness to His will.

 Focus on Jonah 1:11-17. What timeless insight about sin do the sailors' experiences illustrate?

One person's rebellion against God inevita-
bly affects other people. Use your own history, or the experience of someone you
know, to illustrate how one person's disobedience harms innocent parties.

A _____

_____

_____

Jonah 1:17-2:10 reveals God's continued intervention in the prophet's life. Read Chapter 2 carefully.

Q What words/phrases in Jonah 2 reveal a positive shift in Jonah's attitude?

A _____

_____

_____

The unusual "divine curriculum" that God had mapped out for Jonah had its desired effect—Jonah's desperate situation dissolved defiance and softened his heart. "Jonah prayed" (2:1). He said, "I will look again toward Your holy temple" (2:4). While in danger, he "remembered the LORD, and [his] prayer came to [God]" (2:7). Finally, he told the Lord, "I will sacrifice to You with the voice of thanksgiving. That which I have vowed I will pay" (2:9).

Q What lessons about prayer does Jonah 2 offer?

A _____

_____

_____

Even when we have blown it, we can approach the Lord. When our sorrow over sin is genuine,

He extends forgiveness and fellowship with Him
is restored. Too often we hesitate to approach
Him after we have strayed. We question our ac-
ceptability before God and fear His rejection.
Such a mind-set hinders us from offering the very
prayer needed to restore our fellowship with
Him. Praying "in Jesus' name" means our basis
for approaching Him is *Jesus'* merit, not our own.
(*See the discipleship course from Christian Publications titled* Discovering Your Identity. *There
you will examine the various aspects of your position in Christ and the practical implications for
daily living.*)

 To conclude your investigation of Jonah
1-2, complete the "chapter contrasts" exercise below. **Jot down words/phrases
that describe Jonah's attitudes, as implied
by his actions or words. The lists should
expose a stark contrast in his spirit.**

Jonah 1   Jonah 2

_____   _____

_____   _____

_____   _____

_____   _____

_____   _____

Chapter 11 of this book finishes Jonah's story.
You will discover how Jonah fared the second
time he took the test. You will also see the global

shape of God's heart and feel His passion for people who have not heard the gospel.

For now, though, mull over the implications of Jonah 2 for your life.

So What?

Allow God's Spirit to question you through the following probes:

- *Is there any realm of my life in which I am rebelling against God's will as revealed in Scripture or the clear leading of the Holy Spirit?*

- *When I balk at something God says to do, how does my resistance normally show?*

- *How have instances of personal rebellion affected others in the sphere of my influence?*

- *What are the evidences in my life of God's continued love and involvement, in spite of my stubbornness?*

- *How has the Lord acted in the past to get my attention and transform my attitudes toward an assigned task?*

- *Do I need to enter God's presence right now and confess an attempt to avoid His will?*

- *When God gives a seemingly unpleasant assignment, He has a larger priority in mind than my own convenience. His plan for Jonah was ultimately a means of reaching*

thousands of people with the message of sal-
vation. Can I trust God with the bigger pic-
ture and believe that He has a grand
purpose that supersedes my own agenda?

Memorizing Scripture

When God commissioned Jonah, his prejudice against the Assyrians clouded his perspective. In effect, He relied on his own understanding of the situation, rather than God's. By memorizing Proverbs 3:5, you will give the Holy Spirit fuel to work with whenever a divinely assigned task seems unpleasant.

Frequently the unsaved are viewed as enemies rather than victims of the Enemy. Spirituality is viewed as separation from the unsaved. The new Christian is told he has "nothing in common" with his unsaved associates. Quite frankly, I have a lot in common with them: a mortgage, car payments, kids who misbehave, a lawn to mow, a car to wash, a less-than-perfect marriage, a few too many pounds around my waist, and an interest in sports, hobbies and other activities they enjoy. It is well to remember that Jesus was called a "friend of sinners."[1]

—Joe Aldrich

The Test of a World without Christ

I believe in the God of the second chance.

I believe in the God who is not put off by our fiascoes.

I believe in the God who has an uncanny ability to bring good out of disaster.

I believe in the God who puts Humpty Dumpties back together again.[2]

That is how Dean Merrill's book, *The God Who Won't Let Go*, begins. In his book he describes divine grace in the face of failure and wrong choices.

The title of his book is an apt tag for the book of Jonah. Though the prophet hitched a boat ride taking him in the opposite direction from his assigned locale, *God would not let him go.* He pursued Jonah on the open seas, employing a storm to get the prophet's attention and a huge fish to rescue him from certain death. Those experiences increased Jonah's receptivity to the preaching task in Nineveh. After Jonah vented a heartfelt prayer from the fish's stomach, the fish vomited him on the beach—literally giving the prophet grounds for rejoicing.

Chapters 3 and 4 of Jonah reveal "the God of the second chance." He gave Jonah another opportunity to obey. But the real story is God's compassion for the pagan Ninevites. Their wickedness was an abomination to the Lord yet He loved them enough to send a messenger to warn them of the consequences of disregarding Him. God wouldn't let go of Jonah *or* the Ninevites—He gave both parties an undeserved fresh chance.

Just as your faith is sometimes challenged by an unpleasant assignment from God, it is also tested by the plight of a lost world. How you respond to the spiritual needs of twenty-first century "Ninevites" exposes what you believe about God, and whether or not you trust Him to use you to make a difference.

Fresh Chances

Digesting Jonah 3-4 gives you a close-up look at the global-shaped heart of God. After reading Chapters 3 and 4 of Jonah, the questions in this section can help you delve beneath the surface and uncover the timeless elements of the text.

Chapter 2 revealed Jonah's change of heart: when his life was threatened, he refocused his thoughts on God and cried for help. From the fish's belly, he thanked God for the rescue and promised to fulfill his vows.

Q Is a change in our attitude toward God, as reflected in the wording of our prayers, the *primary* proof of repentance? Why or why not?

A _____

_____

_____

Q Glance over Chapter 3 of Jonah again. **What evidences of genuine repentance do you see in Jonah and the Ninevites?**

A _____

_____

_____

For Jonah, the process of repentance began with a contrite heart, renewed prayer life and a sincere vow of recommitment to God (Chapter 2). The process continued with an obedient response to the second command to go to Nineveh (3:2-3).

Evidences of repentance among the Ninevites included participation in a fast (3:7), wearing of sackcloth (3:6-9), prayer for mercy (3:8) and transformed deeds (3:10). Only when "God saw their deeds, that they turned from their wicked way" (3:10) did He relent concerning the warning of calamity.

Behavioral change was the ultimate gauge of repentance in both Jonah and the people of Nineveh. The term "repent" means "to turn," and refers to lifestyle changes spawned by an inward work in the heart. Feeling sorry about our sin is not the same as repenting. *Genuine repentance affects what we do about sin, not merely how we feel about it.*

What follows is an excerpt from an article entitled, "Why Don't Sinners Cry Anymore?" by the late Joe Bayly. What he says emphasizes the need for a heart broken over sin and a contrite spirit that leads to lifestyle transformation.

> British thinker-preacher Martyn Lloyd-Jones commented that people no longer weep at evangelistic meetings. They laugh, he said, they come happily to the front, but they don't mourn over their sins. Nor does the evangelist indicate that weeping, or repentance, is part of a transaction with God.
>
> Godly sorrow for sin that leads to repentance is almost totally absent from our preaching and from our lives. The one who enters the kingdom without repentance hardly finds need for it as a resident. We've lost the ability to say "I'm sorry" to God and to one another. We have lost it as persons and we have lost it as a nation. For if

Christians do not feel the need to repent, shall we expect non-Christians to do so? . . .

The New Testament word for repentance of the kind that pleases God means being sorry enough to change conduct—it involves an about-face. . . . For many years, the *New Yorker* magazine has had two subjects of cartoons repeated again and again. One is Noah's Ark. The other is of a man with a sandwich sign that reads, "Repent. The end of the world is at hand."

I think we need that message—not just in a cartoon, but in our pulpits and in our lives.[3]

Q What is your reaction to Bayly's remarks? Why?

A _____

_____

_____

Q What are some evidences among church people today of a flippant attitude toward sin and repentance?

A _____

_____

_____

Q How should the nature of true repentance affect the content of personal witnessing or public presentations of the gospel?

A _____

_____

_____

Now shift your focus to the events in Jonah 4. **What contrast do you see between Jonah's attitude in Chapter 2 and his inner state as reported in Chapter 4?**

A _____

_____

When God decided not to destroy the Ninevites, Jonah was angry (4:1). He complained to the Lord, suggesting that he did not want God to dispense grace to the city (4:2). Nearly losing his life—then benefitting from the life-saving intervention of God—had previously softened his heart (Chapter 2). That softening resulted in obedience the second time around (3:1-3) but when it became obvious that God had indeed spared the city, bitterness surfaced once again within Jonah. Though Jonah had demonstrated a mark of repentance by preaching in Nineveh, a selfish attitude had crept back into his heart. He vacillated in his yieldedness to God's intentions for the unsaved people of Nineveh.

Read Ephesians 4:32. Paul insisted that the only basis we have for forgiving others is the fact that we have received forgiveness from Christ.

 What contrast do you see between the way God had dealt with Jonah (Jonah 1:17-3:3) and the way Jonah dealt with the Ninevites (4:1-9)?

A _____

_____

Jonah had been on the receiving end of God's compassion. He was a member of the Jewish nation, which had been highly favored by God and the recipient of His special revelation. And, undeservedly, God had given Jonah a second chance to obey the call to go to Nineveh. Jonah did *not* deal with the Ninevites in the gracious way he had been treated by God. Verse 5 of Chapter 4 implies that Jonah was still clinging to the hope that God would destroy Nineveh. He continued to harbor an unforgiving spirit toward a natural enemy of the Jews, forgetting that his own defiance had caused enmity between himself and the Lord. If he had meditated on God's gracious treatment toward himself, perhaps Jonah would have rejoiced, rather than pouted, when Nineveh was spared.

 To summarize, describe how God's grace demonstrated in your past experience is the basis for your outreach to people who are far from Christ.

A _____

_____

_____

Zero in on Jonah 4:5-11. God utilized a plant (4:6), a worm (4:7), the sun (4:8) and a scorching wind (4:8) to hammer a point into Jonah's rather thick head.

What truth was God trying to impress upon Jonah through those object lessons?

Jonah's focus was self-centered. He whined about the discomfort of losing his shade (4:8-9). God's concern was for the lost residents of Nineveh. In Jonah 4:10, God reproved the prophet for channeling his compassion in the wrong direction. He wanted Jonah's commitment to be to this fundamental truth: *the eternal destinies of people should concern us a lot more than temporal matters or personal comfort.* Because God had initiated a special relationship with the Jewish people, they were vulnerable to the germs of bigotry. They often forgot what God had said to the father of their race, Abraham: "*All* peoples on earth will be blessed through you" (Genesis 12:3, NIV, emphasis added). All along, God intended for the Jews to share the good news of His love to the Gentiles.

As you wrap up your investigation of the book of Jonah, ponder the portrait of God painted by Jonah's story. **What does the narrative reveal about Him?**

The punch line of the account of Jonah's experiences is God's compassion for unsaved people. The fresh chance He extended to the prophet was prompted by the larger concern of the eternal welfare of the Ninevites.

The thread of God's compassion weaves its way throughout the four chapters of Jonah. His compassion, as expressed in the calling of Jonah, is revealed in the first three verses of Chapter 1. His concern for their souls is further demonstrated in His pursuit of the rebellious prophet (1:4-10) and in His rescue of Jonah from the sea and the fish's belly (1:17-2:10). By giving Jonah a fresh chance to obey the commission (3:1-4), God's compassion is directed toward the prophet. Then His compassion for the Ninevites was expressed in the cancellation of judgment, occasioned by their repentance (3:5-10). When Jonah sulked as a consequence of the city's being spared (4:1-4), God employed object lessons from nature to explain the significance of His compassion toward Nineveh (4:5-11). Their eternal state took precedence over Jonah's personal preference and comfort.

Contemporary Ninevites

Who are the unbelieving persons in your sphere of influence whom you naturally dislike? Persons who have made no bones about their animosity toward you? Who have either ridiculed your faith or hurt you in some way?

What group of people on the world scene do you consider spiritual foes? People whose behavior is godless or whose opposition to your faith and security is revolting?

The people who come to your mind are contemporary Ninevites. Do you ever pray for their salvation? Do you support and intercede for missionaries who serve among people whom you consider "the enemy"? We are acting too much like Jonah if we sing "Amazing Grace" on Sundays, yet dismiss these "Ninevites" from our lives.

God has not dismissed them. He is not ready to let them go. That's because the circumference of His love is as big as the globe.

Memorizing Scripture

Since the slant of this chapter is God's love for people who do not know Him, hide in your heart a verse that reminds you of His global concern and the part He wants you to play in it: Mark 16:15.

By no stretch of the imagination can the Christian community be called the "salt of the earth." For salt to be effective, it must get out of its container and into the world of hurting, dying, suffering, sinning people. There is no impact without contact, and yet, after knowing the Lord two years, the average Christian has no significant relationships with non-Christians.[1]

—Joe Aldrich

CHAPTER TWELVE

The Test of Sharing Your Faith

In what sense is it a "test" to share your faith with a non-Christian? *If you're afraid to broach the subject of Christ to an unbeliever; if you feel inferior as a witness, figuring God couldn't possibly use you to make a difference; if you doubt whether the Lord can transform the lives of non-Christians you know. . . .*

Personal evangelism may pose a test for which you are unprepared. Your attitude toward witnessing says a lot more about your view of the Lord than it does about your view of yourself. Since He has commissioned you to witness (Matthew 28:18-20), you can trust Him to equip you for what He has called you to do.

Whether your target is a relative, a close friend or someone you would classify as a "modern-day Ninevite," the one-verse approach that follows provides a simple structure for conveying the message.

Before examining the following pages, memorize John 3:16. Be sure to use the New American Standard Bible translation since the one-verse method which follows employs the precise wording from that translation.

The John 3:16 One-Verse Method

What follows is a step-by-step explanation, including diagrams, for using John 3:16 to share the gospel in personal evangelism.

INTRODUCTION

TRANSITION: Say that John 3:16 is the most famous verse in the entire Bible and that you want to show this person why.

ACTION: Take out a piece of paper and write the words of John 3:16 at the very top of the page in this particular order, leaving room on the page for subsequent steps. (To help you remember this order, note that the middle two phrases both start with the word "that" and both end with a reference to Jesus Christ.) Number these phrases in the following order: 1, 3, 4, 2. (See Step 1.)

EXPLANATION: The reason John 3:16 is so famous is because it summarizes the Bible in four spiritual truths. If you understand these four spiritual truths, you will understand what the entire Bible is all about.

John 3:16

1. For God so loved the world,
3. that He gave His only begotten Son,
4. that whoever believes in Him
2. should not perish, but have eternal life.

Step 1: Introduction

GOD'S PURPOSE

TRANSITION: Let's look at the first truth.

ACTION: Put quotation marks around the words "God," "love" and "world." Then, about halfway down the page, diagram this truth by writing the word "God" on the right, the word "world" on the left, and the word "love" down the middle. (See Step 2.)

John 3:16

1. For "God" so "love"d the "world,"
3. that He gave His only begotten Son,
4. that whoever believes in Him
2. should not perish, but have eternal life.

WORLD   L   GOD
                 O
                 V
                 E

Step 2: God's Purpose

EXPLANATION: God created man to have a personal relationship with Him. He wants this relationship to be one of love, one where God shows His love to people and where people show their love to Him.

TRANSITION: Why do you think that more people are not experiencing this loving personal relationship?
ACTION: Write the word "sin" below the word "love." Then draw two cliffs, one under the word "world," and the other under the word "God." (See Step 3.)

John 3:16

1. For "God" so "love"d the "world,"
3. that He gave His only begotten Son,
4. that whoever believes in Him
2. should not perish, but have eternal life.

WORLD   L   GOD
                         O
                         V
                         E

                        SIN

Step 3

EXPLANATION: It is because of sin. Sin is disobeying God. When someone is offended it causes problems in the relationship. Sin causes a separation between God and man.

MAN'S PROBLEM

TRANSITION: Let's look at the second spiritual truth. It says, "should not perish, but have eternal life."

ACTION: Put quotation marks around the word "perish" and write it under the left-hand cliff, the one with the word "world" on it. Then draw an arrow downward from the word "perish" and write the word "hell." (See Step 4.)

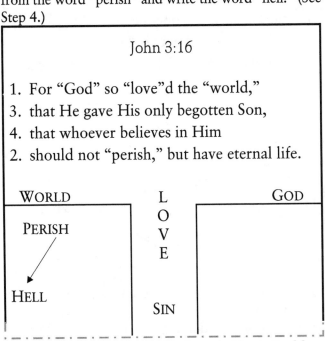

Step 4: Man's Problem

EXPLANATION: It is bad enough to be separated from God and His love, but it gets worse. The Bible says that if anyone dies physically while spiritually separated from God, he will spend eternity in a place called hell.

TRANSITION: That's bad news, but this second spiritual truth also gives some good news.

ACTION: Put quotation marks around the words "eternal life" and write them under the right-hand cliff. Draw an arrow downward and write the word "heaven." (See Step 5.)

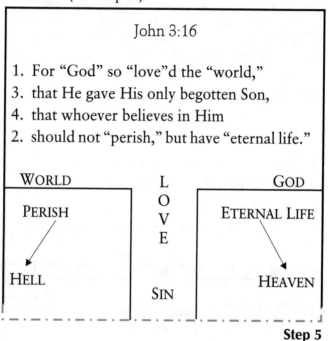

Step 5

EXPLANATION: The good news is that God does not want man to spend eternity in hell. His desire is to have a personal relationship with man so that they can live together forever in a place called heaven.

GOD'S REMEDY

TRANSITION: The question then becomes: How does one deal with his problem of sin? That leads us to the third spiritual truth.

ACTION: Put quotation marks around the word "Son" and write it on the diagram so that it shares the word "love." Then draw a cross that encloses the words "Son" and "love" and bridge the two cliffs. (See Step 6.)

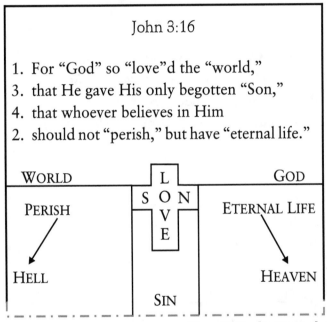

John 3:16

1. For "God" so "love"d the "world,"
3. that He gave His only begotten "Son,"
4. that whoever believes in Him
2. should not "perish," but have "eternal life."

WORLD   L   GOD
          S O N
PERISH   V   ETERNAL LIFE
          E

HELL   HEAVEN

SIN

Step 6: God's Remedy

EXPLANATION: God took care of the sin problem by sending His Son, Jesus Christ, to live a perfect life, then die on the cross in order that a person's sin could be forgiven. The amazing thing is after Jesus was dead and buried, He rose from the dead, proving God has the power to save people from a destiny of torment.

MAN'S RESPONSE

TRANSITION: The question now is, how can a person cross over the bridge that Christ has provided? The fourth spiritual truth gives the answer.

ACTION: Draw an arrow from the word "world" to the word "God." Put quotation marks around the words "believes in Him" and write them on top of the arrow. (See Step 7.)

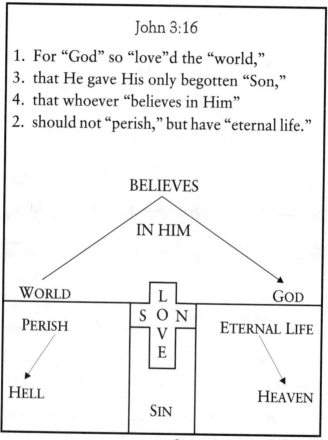

John 3:16

1. For "God" so "love"d the "world,"
3. that He gave His only begotten "Son,"
4. that whoever "believes in Him"
2. should not "perish," but have "eternal life."

BELIEVES

IN HIM

WORLD   L   GOD

S O N

PERISH   V   ETERNAL LIFE

E

HELL   HEAVEN

SIN

Step 7: Man's Response

EXPLANATION: It is not enough to simply know (1) that God loves you, (2) that your sin keeps you from that love and will ultimately send you to hell and (3) that Jesus Christ's death on the cross spares you from it all. It is only as you believe in Christ as your Lord and Savior that you cross over the separation caused by your sin and begin a personal relationship with God. This word "believe" is more than just believing in Abraham Lincoln. It means to commit everything you know about yourself to everything you know about Christ. It means to trust Christ and Him alone to make you right with God.

INVITATION

TRANSITION: May we personalize this for a moment?

ACTION: Draw a circle around the word "whoever," then write the word "whoever" above the phrase "believes in Him." (See Step 8.)

EXPLANATION: The Bible says whoever believes in Him will cross over to God and receive eternal life. Where would you place yourself on this diagram?

- If they put themselves on the right-hand side, ask them to tell you about when and how they crossed over.

- If they put themselves on the left-hand side, or on top of the cross, ask the next question.

- Do you see anything keeping you from placing your faith in Christ and crossing over to God right now?

- If they say "yes," ask them what their questions are and deal with them accordingly. If you do not know the answer to a question, tell them you will try to find out.

• If they say "no," prepare to lead them in prayer expressing their desire to God.

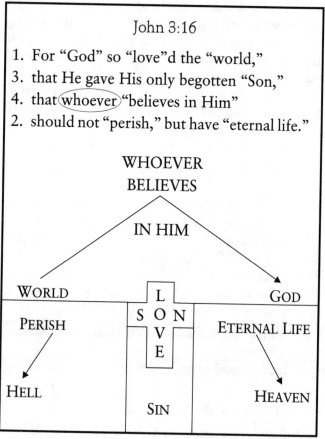

John 3:16

1. For "God" so "love"d the "world,"
3. that He gave His only begotten "Son,"
4. that whoever "believes in Him"
2. should not "perish," but have "eternal life."

WHOEVER
BELIEVES

IN HIM

WORLD   GOD

L
PERISH   S O N   ETERNAL LIFE
V
E

HELL   HEAVEN

SIN

Step 8: Invitation

PRAYER OF SALVATION

TRANSITION: If you desire to place your faith in Christ to make you right with God, it's as easy as 1, 2, 3, 4.

ACTION: Put the number 1 under the right-hand cliff, the number 2 under the left-hand cliff, the number 3 under the cross, and the number 4 beside the word "whoever." (See Step 9.)

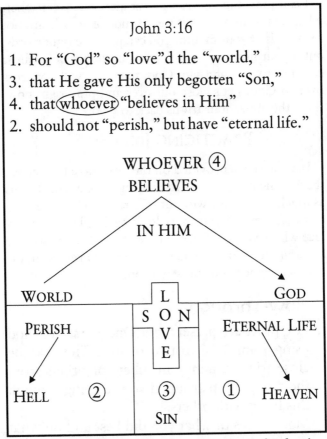

John 3:16

1. For "God" so "love"d the "world,"
3. that He gave His only begotten "Son,"
4. that (whoever) "believes in Him"
2. should not "perish," but have "eternal life."

WHOEVER ④

BELIEVES

IN HIM

WORLD   GOD

PERISH   ETERNAL LIFE

L
S O N
O
V
E

HELL   ②   ③   ①   HEAVEN

SIN

Step 9: Prayer of Salvation

EXPLANATION: If you would like to trust Christ you can do so right now. Tell God: 1) that you are grateful that He loves you, 2) that you are sorry for your sin that has separated you from His love, 3) that you are grateful that He gave His only Son to die on the cross and to forgive your sin and 4) that you believe Christ will make you right with Him right now.

I can pray and you can repeat after me. Remember, what is most important is the attitude of your heart, not the words of your mouth. You can pray the right words, but if your heart is not truly convinced that only Christ can make you right with God, then you will not cross over to God. Let's close our eyes and pray right now. (Pray the above four truths back to God.)

PRACTICING John 3:16

Use the space provided on the next page to practice sharing the message of Christ using John 3:16. Do this as much as possible without referring back to the various diagrams. If you must look back, place a smiley face where you got stuck. These smiley faces will serve as a reminder to you where you need to review in order to enhance your presentation.

Follow-Through

1. For practice, present the One-Verse Method using John 3:16 to two people. They can be close friends, family members or others from the discipleship group, if you're going through this book with others.
2. Make notes of what you did best and on what needs more work.
3. Look for opportunities to build friendships or talk to non-Christians.

Memorzing Scripture

To expedite your use of the One-Verse Method, memorize John 3:16 from the New American Standard version of the Bible.

Epilogue

Looking Back . . . Going Forward

Congratulations! You have completed twelve book chapters that examined various "tests of faith." You have discovered that God often challenges or exposes the extent of your trust in Him for the ultimate purpose of solidifying it. He employs a wide variety of circumstances to expose your weakness, but His strength; your need, but His sufficiency; your spiritual bankruptcy, but His endless resources. When you arrive at wit's end, you find yourself at the beginning of His wisdom.

You have learned that the key to cultivating a deeper faith is to become more intimate with its object: Jesus Christ. That is why the product of stronger faith is forged in the crucible of daily experience—so you can learn to trust in Him, to discover His love and adequacy, outside a Bible classroom or church sanctuary.

Whether your faith test is an enticement to sin, adverse circumstances, stinging criticism, an unpleasant task, personal pain, sharing your faith for the first time, some type of grand success or an experience not covered in this book, rest assured that God wants you to pass these exams! And He is willing, through the indwelling presence of the Holy Spirit, to serve as your personal tutor along the way.

ENDNOTES

CHAPTER 1 - The Test of Temptation
1. Merrill Tenney, *Roads a Christian Must Travel*, (Wheaton, IL: Tyndale House, 1979), pp. 23-24.
2. S. Craig Glickman, *Knowing Christ* (Chicago: Moody Press, 1980), n.p.
3. Ibid.
4. Jay Kesler, *I Never Promised You a Disneyland* (Waco, TX: Word Books, n.d.), p. 59.

CHAPTER 2 - The Test of Stormy Circumstances
1. From Ron Dunn, in a sermon delivered to Campus Crusade staff during a conference in Colorado Springs, CO, 1976.

CHAPTER 3 - The Test of Hopeless Situations
1. *Group*, September 1984, p. A-16.

CHAPTER 4 - The Test of Praying Distinctively
1. David Bryant, from a chapel message given to the student body of Columbia International University.
2. Charles Swindoll, *Seasons of Life* (Portland, OR: Multnomah Press, 1983), p. 382.
3. Richard Foster, *Prayer: Finding the Heart's True Home* (San Francisco, CA: Harper Collins, 1992), p. 179.
4. Ibid., p. 181.

CHAPTER 6 - The Test of Personal Pain
1. John Piper, *Desiring God* (Sisters, OR: Multnomah Books, 1996), p. 216.
2. Lloyd Shearer, "Children Who Feel No Pain." Intelligence Report, *Parade* magazine, February 12, 1989, pp. 18-19.
3. Perry Downs, as quoted in Lynn Garrett, "Mending Broken Wings," *Wellspring*, Fall 1989, pp. 83-85.
4. James I. Packer, *Knowing God* (Downers Grove, IL: InterVarsity Press, 1973), p. 222.

5. Ibid., p. 227.

CHAPTER 7 - The Test of Responding to Criticism

1. Gordon MacDonald, *Restoring Your Spiritual Passion* (Nashville, TN: Oliver-Nelson, 1986), pp. 192-193.

2. Ibid., pp. 189-191.

3. Gordon MacDonald, *Ordering Your Private World*, expanded edition (Nashville, TN: Oliver-Nelson, 1984), p. 106.

CHAPTER 8 - The Test of Discouraging News

1. Foster, p. 191.

2. J. Sidlow Baxter, *Explore the Book* (in one volume) (Grand Rapids, MI: Zondervan, 1960), p. 232.

CHAPTER 10 - The Test of an Unpleasant Task

1. From a chapel message by Robertson McQuilkin delivered to the student body of Columbia International University, 1998.

2. The maxim, "God does not allow His children to sin successfully" was inspired by the writing of Charles H. Spurgeon, as quoted in Arnold Dallimore, *Spurgeon* (Carlisle, PA: The Banner of Truth Trust, 1985), p. 14.

CHAPTER 11 - The Test of a World without Christ

1. Joe Aldrich, *Lifestyle Evangelism* (Portland, OR: Multnomah Press, 1981), p. 20.

2. Dean Merrill, *The God Who Won't Let Go* (Grand Rapids, MI: Zondervan, 1998), p. 13.

3. Joe Bayly, "Why Don't Sinners Cry Anymore?" *Eternity*, October 1974, pp. 71-72.

CHAPTER 12 - The Test of Sharing Your Faith

1. Aldrich, p. 19.

MEMORY VERSES

Terry Powell teaches Christian education and Bible at Columbia International University, Columbia, SC. You may contact him at: tpowell@ciu.edu.

Bill Jones is president of Crossover Communications International. Crossover is a missions organization helping to fulfill the Great Commission in Eurasia, currently focusing on the countries in the area of the Black Sea. Bill also serves as the program director for the Master of Arts in Missions and the Master of Arts in Leadership at Columbia International University in Columbia, South Carolina. A passionate communicator, Bill has trained thousands of people all around the world how to effectively share their faith in Christ.

CROSSOVER
COMMUNICATIONS
INTERNATIONAL

P.O. Box 211755   Columbia, SC 29221
Phone: 803-691-0688   Fax: 803-691-9355
www.crossoverusa.org

Write to Terry Powell or Bill Jones at:
CIU
P.O. Box 3122
Columbia, SC 29230
or call (803) 754-4100